12-7-1988

Around the Horn and Home Again

AND OTHER TALES

Around the Horn and Home Again

AND OTHER TALES

BY

SHALIMAR

(F. C. HENDRY)

William Blackwood & Sons Ltd.

Edinburgh and London

First Impression . . .	*June* 1929
Second Impression . . .	*December* 1929
Popular Edition . . .	*September* 1932
Reprinted . . .	*January* 1935

CONTENTS.

Around the Horn and
Home Again.

" Around the Horn and home again,
For that's the sailor's way."

—*Old Sea Song.*

I. FULL AND BY.

I.

" FULL and by."

The man at the wheel passed me the order,
relinquished his grip on the spokes, and took a step
sideways, while I, who had just come up on the
poop and had been standing behind him, took over
the steering.

" Full and by it is," I replied.

It had been a perfect relief. Looking aloft I
could see the weather clew of the mizzen royal just
quivering, showing that the vessel was steering as
high into the wind as she would go consistent with
making the best of her way through the water. All
the sails below that were full of wind and firm, for
the upper yards were braced in more than the lower

A

ones, and the upper sails would therefore be the first to shake as she came up into the wind.

There was a moderate breeze from the north-west, and the large four-masted barque on which I was the senior apprentice had just cleared the Strait of Le Maire—between Staten Land and Tierra del Fuego—through which we had been helped by a strong tide, and now with all sail set she was stretching out on the starboard tack for Cape Horn. Not far astern were the two islands between which we had just passed, high, barren, and inhospitable, their lofty peaks covered with snow, and not a sign of habitation anywhere. Although it was spring the wind came blowing down cold from those dreary mountain tops.

During my two hours' trick at the wheel, from four o'clock in the afternoon until six, the vessel was laying quite a good course, almost parallel with the Tierra del Fuego coast. The wind was fairly steady in direction, varying not more than a point, and the captain as he paced the weather side of the poop seemed to be well satisfied with life, although one could see that he was anxious. And small wonder : on the events of that day and the next would depend, to a great extent, the length of the passage which his vessel would make. Rounding Cape Horn outward bound, to the westward, was one of the most trying and difficult jobs which the windjammer shipmaster had to face ; he had everything against him ; for ten months of the year the wind varies from north-west to south-west, but always with westing in it, and for the greater part of the time those winds are of gale force. Sweeping without let or hindrance from any land right round the globe, those westerly winds raise tremendous seas, which are ever exerting their opposing power on the unfortunate outward-bounder, and in addition they create a surface current also hostile to progress to the westward. On this occasion it rather looked as if we were getting a chance. If the wind held as it was then for a couple of days and we could win as far west as 75° longitude, we were pretty certain to get round the Horn successfully.

On my relief from the wheel at six o'clock I went into our little half-deck for our scanty evening meal. We apprentices were accommodated in a deck-house which stood between the break of the poop and the mizzen-mast. It was built of iron, lined with wood in the way of the bunks, and its only furniture consisted of eight of those bunks and a table, which slid up and down on two wooden stanchions, and spent most of its time suspended close to the roof, for we preferred to sit on our sea-chests for our meals, with our plates on our knees. This half-deck, with its separate accommodation from the crew, was about the only privilege we got in return for the large premiums which our parents had paid in order to have us trained as officers of the Mercantile Marine, and it was a very mixed blessing. In bad weather it was usually half full of water, and we often envied the sailors, who were comfortably housed in dry quarters underneath the forecastle head, and had, in cold weather, a bogey stove. Apart from the separate accommodation we were fed and treated much as they were ; in fact we often had to work harder, and much of the menial work fell to our lot. It has been said that a former Viceroy of India, when he was an apprentice in a full-rigged ship, had to clean out the pig-sty, and I can well believe it. If there was a pig on board, the youngest apprentice would certainly have to do it. Being in the fourth and last year of my apprenticeship I had rather got beyond that, and took my regular trick at the wheel and turn on the look-out with the able seamen.

On that evening after we had finished our meal our sole topic of conversation was our chance of getting quickly round the Horn and away north into fine weather again, for we were bound to San Francisco. The second dog-watch in a sailing vessel was the time when all hands were free except for those actually at work, and moreover, it was the only time throughout the night or day when some one was not trying to snatch some precious sleep. Although the weather was cold the lee door of the half-deck was open for two reasons—to allow the clouds of tobacco smoke to escape, and to enable the apprentices of the port watch, whose turn of duty on deck it was, to be with us and yet be ready to spring out on deck when an order was issued. Presently the boatswain, a cheerless Cockney, smoking a pessimistic pipe, came along and leant against it.

" It looks as if we were in for a good slant, Bo'sun," I remarked.

" Huh," replied the petty officer, " I remember when I was bo'sun of the old *Swatow* we came through the Straits just the same and thought we was in for a slant. Two months after that we was still beatin' about the 'Orn."

" Well, we won't be two months this time," chirped the youngest apprentice cheerfully.

" Won't we ? Don't you be so bloomin' sure, me young know-all," responded the boatswain gloomily as he drifted away.

The next morning we were still slipping along almost laying our course ; there was a fresh breeze with alternate intervals of sunshine and cloud. Just after daylight came in, two small white clouds were sighted right ahead ; they grew into towering pillars of canvas ; the breeze freshened and it was necessary for us to take in the royals, but those two pillars, ever growing in height, showed no signs of shortening down. Presently we discovered that they were two full-rigged ships, one painted green, the other black. They were distant about three miles apart from each other, leaning over, and coming along with broad white splashes of foam at their bows. One of them turned out to be one of the famous Aberdeen White Star wool clippers from Australia ; the other a German, one of the more modern P. line of Hamburg, doubtless from one of the nitrate ports of Chile. What a spectacle they made—the finest action picture that I have ever seen. Even at that time—toward the end of last century—such spectacles were gradually becoming rarer ; to-day all but one or two of those lovely clippers have vanished from the face of the waters, and such a sight will probably never be seen again.

Certain sentimental writers, regretting the passing

of the old days of sail, suggest that many men in steamers would willingly give up their well-fed, well-paid jobs, to be back again in windjammers. Quite recently I read a poem about two old sailors sitting in the bar-parlour of a public-house who were apparently dying for the opportunity to jockey a weather yard-arm and once again haul out the reef-earing of an upper top-sail in a blinding snow squall off the Horn. Possibly it may have been the beer talking ; on the other hand, there may be such men, although I have never met them ; indeed I have never known any one who, having once weathered Cape Horn outward bound, showed any eagerness whatever to repeat the performance ; many did so year after year from necessity—few, I fancy, from choice. Yet, with all that, I cannot imagine any man who has ever served on a sailing vessel not being willing to give much to see again such a vivid breath-catching spectacle as the approach of those two ships. The Aberdeen vessel was leading slightly—of the two she seemed to be the daintier, to have more breeding. She passed close to windward of us, so that as she heeled over toward us we could see her deck-houses and half of her polished main deck. Her hull was painted green, with a gilt stripe, and there were gilded scrolls around her white figurehead and her elliptical stern ; those parts of her masts and yards which we could see—for most of them were partially obscured by her swelling canvas—were painted white. With the wind two points abaft her beam, every sail was drawing, and she was flying twenty-five of them, seventeen square sails and eight fore and afters. Her sharp wedge-like bow was shearing cleanly through the blue waves, flinging them aside so that they turned into foam which raced creaming along her side, and she was walking through the water like a thing of life. Most of the time her lee scuppers were awash ; when she rolled lightly to windward against her towering press of canvas we could see the water gushing from them ; then she would lean farther over until her lee rail was almost dipping as she flew past.

The German passed us to leeward a little farther away. Being to windward of her we could see her masts, spars, and rigging standing out distinctly against her white canvas. She appeared to be stiffer than the other vessel. Leaning well over away from us so that a great part of her pink boot-topping was visible below her sombre black side, she hardly seemed to roll at all but tore along steadily. Aloft and below she gave the impression of great power—a weight-carrying hunter as compared with the more flexible thorough-bred racer which had just passed by on the other side.

When they were about a couple of miles astern a squall, bringing with it snow and sleet, struck us, and in it the wind shifted to the west, causing us to break off four points from our course and to take in still more canvas. We were still steering full and by, but were heading far more to the south than we were to the west. When the squall cleared, the two vessels were hull down astern, and the two white clouds of canvas quickly dwindled away and dissolved on the eastern horizon. With the exception of one vessel, which we could very well have done without, those were the last sails we were destined to see for many weary weeks.

II.

For the next six weeks gale succeeded gale, and ever the wind was from the west. The waves lifted themselves up in long ridges with deep dark hollows between them ; they ran high and fast, tossing their white caps in the air, solidly resisting our every attempt to get to the westward. Backwards and forwards, mostly under short canvas and with the yards braced hard on the backstays, we went across the face of that lonely waste of waters. South we would go on the starboard tack until we were almost on the fringe of the Antarctic ice, then north again on the other tack sometimes to sight the lonely bleak Diego Ramirez rocks, sometimes the mainland. To most of us those infrequent glimpses of the land gave the only clue to our progress. Once we discovered after a week's hard tussle that we had made twenty miles ; then we lost it all and more as the gale increased in fury. It was hopeless, weary, heart-breaking work.

The conditions on board during this long-drawn-out misery were such as, fortunately, sailormen of to-day rarely see. The vessel had a cargo of coal, and had left a Bristol Channel port loaded right down to her marks. Moreover, the coal had not been too well stowed ; too much of it was in the lower hold, with the result that she was stiff, inclined to roll heavily, and inert and lifeless in a sea-way. In bad weather the waves simply poured in torrents over her; for the greater part of the time she was like a half-tide rock, and the main deck was usually full of water. Life-lines had been stretched between the forecastle and the break of the poop, but those did not always save us, for in hauling on the braces on the many occasions on which we wore round on to the other tack we would often be up to our necks in the rushing icy water, and sometimes several of us, losing our footing, would be swept writhing against the lee bulwarks. Modern sailing ships were never over-manned, and when a few of the crew, mostly foreigners, developed a form of malingering known as Cape Horn fever, it came very hard on the rest of us. There were, of course, many genuine cases of men suffering from cramp, cuts aggravated by salt water, and bruises.

During those days our half-deck had usually two feet of water swishing around its floor. This water mainly came in below the weather door and at the sides, and those it was impossible to caulk, for the weather door of to-day would be the lee door—the one we used—of to-morrow, when we would go on the other tack. Where the iron plates of the house had sweated on the inside they were now a mass of ice; our blankets were wet; we seldom had a dry stitch of clothing; indeed we never would have had any but for the fact that the cook would occasionally take pity on us and good-naturedly dry stockings or shirts for us at the galley fire. Four hours on and four hours off duty was the regular routine in sailing ships, but it was seldom during that time that we

got our full watch below. That was usually broken
into at the change of the watch, for all hands were
needed for most jobs just then, and often in the
middle of our watch below, or what was even worse,
when we had just got into our bunks and sunk into
a heavy slumber, that dread cry of " all hands on
deck "—an order which, for all the many times that
I had heard it, never failed in bad weather to thrill
me with mingled excitement and dread—would
bring us wearily out into the howling biting wind
and rushing water again.

One of the few bright spots in life was the fact
that we got as an extra ration in cold weather,
porridge for breakfast—" burgoo " the sailors called
it. Usually for that meal we only got biscuits and
coffee, depending for anything else on what was left
over of the previous day's issue of salt beef or pork
—a highly improbable item for the breakfast menu,
as mythical indeed as " the unexpended portion
of the day's ration " of military fame. We received
our whack of " burgoo " at the lee door of the
galley, where the cook ladled it into a wooden wash-
deck bucket, which one of us took along for its
reception, and on two tragic occasions we lost it.
Tommy, the first voyage apprentice of the starboard watch, had, on the first occasion, been caught
by a heavier sea than usual breaking over the
weather rail, and although he desperately clung
with one hand to the life-line, he was eventually
washed into the lee scuppers, taking our bucket of
" burgoo " with him. On the second occasion he
had just reached the lee door of the half-deck,
which I was holding open for him, when he was

swept off his feet, with the same result. After that we evolved a better plan. In heavy weather either George, who was in his third year, or myself would bring the bucket of " burgoo " from the galley. We would watch our chance and jump on to the main hatch. From there we would dash to the mizzen fife rail and pass the bucket up to Tommy, who would be on the top of the house, and who would then lower it down through the skylight to whichever of us was waiting inside the half-deck for it.

For the whole of one wild night—I don't think that I have ever known a wilder—we lay hove-to with only one sail set out of the twenty-five which we could carry. This was the main lower top-sail —a narrow sodden strip of canvas straining furiously at its chain sheets—which helped to steady the vessel as she lay rising, falling, and rolling in the trough of the sea. So continuously did the waves come crashing over the weather rail that it was almost impossible to pass along the main deck, and for the greater part of the night all hands were clustered on the poop. The wind shrieked from out of the south-west, making a weird din in the rigging, and bringing with it furious squalls of hail and snow. Movement about the poop was impossible. We could only hang on to the rails, wet, cold, and un-utterably miserable, waiting for the hours of dark-ness to pass.

The long-delayed dawn came at last, revealing a blue-lipped, red-eyed, half-frozen group of suffer-ing humanity, and with it the wind seemed to lull a little and the squalls were less frequent and not quite so furious. There was still too much wind for more sail to be set, but the captain considered it safe for the watch below to seek their quarters in forecastle and half-deck. About six o'clock we saw the only pleasing sight of that wretched morning—smoke from the galley funnel blowing straight down into the waves to leeward. The fire had been washed out the previous afternoon, but now there seemed to be a prospect of coffee. Vile stuff it would be, but it would be hot and it would make us feel like men again. While we were eagerly watching for a signal from the galley to say that it was ready, the weather clew of the mizzen lower topsail blew free from its containing gaskets and flapped furiously around the yard-arm. Four of the able seamen went up to secure it, and we watched them as they gingerly made their way up the mizzen rigging, being almost flattened against it by the force of the gale. Shrouds and backstays for thirty feet above the deck were now about six inches in diameter, for the spray, which had been lashing against them, had frozen, and as more spray struck them they were gradually thickening into solid bars of ice. It was impossible for the men to hang on to them as they would have done in the usual way, so that they had to adopt the unseamanlike trick, condemned in greenhorns and first-voyagers, of hanging on to the ratlines with their hands as well as their feet—for ratlines have been known to carry away.

Very cautiously they crawled up the rigging and eventually made their way out to the yard-arm. They had some difficulty in securing the sail, for, although only a small portion of it had broken adrift, the canvas was frozen and stiff, and the wind made it act as if it were possessed of devils. At last they mastered it and got it secured again; three of them were laying in along the yard when the fourth, gazing to windward, stretched out his arm toward the weather beam and we could see that he was shouting something. Our eyes followed his directing arm, the sky was fairly clear at the time, and presently we could see through the driving spray tall masts and narrow strips of canvas. Those developed, and we soon discovered that the vessel which was bearing down upon us was another large four-masted barque, running before the wind—homeward bound.

Here was company at last—however brief—after our weeks of loneliness, but we soon noticed that our captain was watching the oncoming vessel with a certain amount of uneasiness. At times she would be heading straight for us, then she would yaw wildly a couple of points and look as if she were making to pass under our stern, only to swing violently a moment afterwards and head across our bow. In the main, however, her line of progression was straight toward us. She was carrying three lower top-sails and a reefed fore-sail, and coming on at a great speed. We also began to feel uneasy and watched her carefully; surely, we thought, those on board must have seen us; the fore-sail being reefed, there was a wide gap between the foot of it and the forecastle head, and they could easily see under it, besides which, when she yawed, we must have been plainly visible on either

side of it. As was only natural, the captain was
the first to solve the problem as his quick shout—

" Hard up the helm—hand to the lee wheel,"
showed.

Being nearest I jumped to the lee side of the
wheel and helped the regular helmsman to heave it
hard over, and while we were holding it like that
I also realised what was wrong with the stranger—
she was unmanageable ; she could not keep out of
our way. In such a wind and sea she should really
have been hove-to, but her captain—doubtless
anxious to take advantage of the fair wind—had
run her too long, with the result that he could
not heave her to now if he wished to. He *had* to
run, and doubtless her heaving helmsmen were
doing their best to keep her dead before the wind,
for if it got too far out on one side or the other she
would broach-to, and in that sea would probably
have foundered or at the least have been dismasted.

Article 21 of the ' Regulations for Preventing
Collision at Sea ' reads : " When by any of these
Rules one of two vessels is to keep out of the way,
the other shall keep her course and speed." Another
of the Articles, however, goes on to say that under
certain conditions a departure from these Rules
may be necessary in order to avoid immediate
danger. The oncoming vessel was running free
while we were close hauled—she was therefore the
giving way vessel, but this was clearly a case in
which we must depart from the Rules, for the
danger was not only immediate but now only too
obvious. When the captain gave his order I doubt
if he, or any one else, thought about the Rules at

all—I certainly didn't, although, as I was reading for my forthcoming examination, they were fresh in my mind ;—he was simply a seaman endeavouring to the best of his ability to save his ship, and indeed had a collision occurred then his action would never have been questioned. There would have been no courts of inquiry or, if there had been, not a soul on board of either of those two ships would have attended it, for the very simple reason that, under those circumstances, there would have been no survivors.

The strange vessel came plunging on ; our own vessel was taking no notice of her helm—she had no way upon her ; something must be set forward to pay her head off.

" Get the foretopmast stay-sail on her, mister," the captain shouted to the second mate. " Quick, men, for your lives."

It was the first time that any of the men had heard the captain add anything of that nature to an order, and it quickened their already obvious anxiety. From the wheel we could see them as, led by the second mate, they dashed down the poop ladder and splashed as best they could along the main deck, clinging to life-lines or fife rails as a great comber swept over the rail and checked their progress. On they went again, reached the forecastle head, and, bending low against the furious wind, proceeded to loose the sail. Would they be in time ? Would the stay-sail stand ? Well, it was brand-new, having only been bent a fortnight before to replace another which had been blown away. The second mate was handling it carefully ;

foot by foot the head of it seemed to crawl up the
stay. When it was half-way up the pressure of the
wind on it began slowly to pay the vessel's head
off ; by the time that they got the sheet fast she
was swinging so quickly that we had to meet her
with the helm. As soon as the wind came abeam
she commenced forging ahead.

By this time the homeward bounder had got very
close. For one sickening moment, perched on the
crest of a great Cape Horn greybeard, she swerved
straight toward us. Then she righted, swung
violently back the other way, and came crashing
past our stern less than fifty yards away—exactly
over the place where we had been two minutes
before. We could read her name and port of
registry on her stern : she was French, a fine great
vessel with black topsides, black ports painted on
a broad white streak, and below the streak she was
lead coloured. As her poop came abreast of our
stern we could see that, as had been the case with
us a short time before, all hands were clustered on
it, most of them clad in yellow oilskins. Two men
were grinding at her wheel ; another, obviously
her captain, staggered down to her port rail and
shouted something, the only word we could catch
being " *Merci.*" He accompanied his shout, however, by the most expressive gesture that I have
ever seen. It plainly implied : " I know that I
should have kept out of your way, but you see
how it is. What could I do ? "

Our captain cordially waved his hand in reply.
He was far too good a seaman to try and find fault
under those circumstances, and besides, he never

knew when he might find himself in the same predicament. Hardly had the Frenchman cleared us
when the wind lulled still more, and presently
above its roar came the triumphant yell of one
who had overcome great difficulties.

" *Ho—coffee !* " shouted the cook.

III.

For fully a fortnight after the episode of the
homeward bounder we were still beating about,
tack for tack, somewhere on the meridian of 68°
west. It looked as if, like the *Flying Dutchman*
and the albatrosses, we were doomed to spend the
rest of our lives down in those latitudes. The south-
west gale to which we had been lying-to died away,
and was promptly succeeded by a north-west one,
which at its height had changed to the south-west
again. Would a slant never come ? We had almost
given up thinking about it.

It came at last, when we apprentices of the starboard watch were in our bunks. When we had
left the deck at four o'clock in the morning the
wind had been from the south-west and moderating.
Doubtless, we thought, it will die away, come
again from the north-west, and the same dreary
system of gales will be repeated. The weather
being fairly fine, there had been no impediment
to sleep, so we were slumbering as if dead when at
seven bells, twenty minutes past seven, the first
voyage apprentice of the other watch thrust his
head in through the lee door and uttered the usual

obnoxious yell which invited us to rise from our
bunks, get breakfast, and prepare for another spell
of duty.

"Now then, you sleepers, seven bells," he
shouted.

I groaned, turned over miserably, and wondered
if I could snatch another five minutes' sleep ; the
unwelcome intruder had his eye upon me. Again
his horrible high-pitched voice echoed through the
little half-deck.

"Now then, you sleepers, seven bells. Turn out
and see what the port watch has done for you."

As my thoughts gradually grew clearer something in the tone of the youthful apprentice's voice
made me sit up in my bunk.

"You seem to be very uppish this morning,
Ginger," I said at last, rather sleepily. "What
has the port watch done for us ? "

"Brought you a fair wind," replied Ginger
promptly.

"A *fair wind !* " I ejaculated incredulously ; I
was now wide awake.

Before the young apprentice could make any
further comment, George, who occupied the bunk
beneath mine, chipped in.

"Ginger," he said, " if this is a leg pull, God help
you. I'll hide the soul casing off you."

"Leg pull be damned," replied the youthful
Ginger, who evidently thought that as a bearer of
good news he should be exempt from hidings, " it's
a fair wind I tell you. Don't be so beastly lazy—
get up and see."

Something told us that even the irreverent Ginger

would not make a joke on such a sacred subject
as a fair wind, and besides, the vessel had a different
motion to anything she had had for weeks ; she
seemed to be going along steadily and smoothly,
more on an even keel. Dressing was a simple
matter ; in those waters we slept all standing, so
all we had to do was to pull on our sea-boots and
pea-jackets and we were ready. We tramped along
the dry deck to the galley with our hook-pots for
coffee, Tommy with the " burgoo " bucket bringing
up the rear. As soon as we had got outside the
half-deck we had seen that the glad tidings were
true ; the yards were off the backstays at last, the
wind was well abaft the beam, and all sail was set.
The faces of those of the watch on deck whom we
met were wreathed in smiles.

" Good-morning, Cookie," said George cheerfully,
as we reached the galley door, " a fair wind, eh ? "

" A bloomin' good job too," replied the cook
pleasantly. " I'm fed up with seein' you brass-
bounders' dirty rags hangin' all over my galley."

Before we returned to the half-deck for our breakfast we discovered that no fewer than five vessels
were in sight, all outward bound. We wondered
where they had all sprung from. One of them, we
were told, had signalled us ; she was a Norwegian
barque with which we had been in company off the
Plate. She must have arrived in the vicinity of the
Horn much about the same time as we did, and it
was certain that we had crossed each other's tracks
a dozen times as we had battled to and fro. Possibly
one dark night, in a bitter snow squall, we might
have passed within a mile of each other.

It was again my trick at the wheel at eight o'clock. As I mounted the poop on the lee side and glanced at the man at the wheel I further realised this wonderful thing which had happened to us : his eye was no longer on the weather clew of the mizzen royal, but was directed at the compass card in the binnacle. " Full and by," the order which had been reiterated day after day for six weary weeks, was a thing of the past. We were steering a compass course at last ; going in the direction in which we wished to go, not merely as near to it as the wind would allow ; heading toward our port. I crossed over, and the man whom I was relieving relinquished the spokes. There was a ring of triumph in his voice as he loudly passed me the helm orders.

" West-nor'-west," he pronounced deliberately, deliciously mouthing the words.

It had again been a perfect relief. The W.N.W. point of the compass card seemed to be glued to the lubber-line in the binnacle.

" West-nor'-west, it is," I replied as I gripped the wheel.

II. RUNNING FREE.

Six months later, having in the meantime been to San Francisco, where we had discharged our coal and loaded a cargo of wheat, we were again in the vicinity of the Horn—homeward bound. This time, however, we were steering east, so that the prevailing winds, the high rushing ridges, and the surface drift would all be in our favour. We had every reason to expect a fair wind, and we got it—indeed one night we got rather too much of it, and under three lower top-sails we flew before the fury of a north-west gale. Before long we were in much the same condition as the Frenchman whom we had met when we were outward bound. We had run the vessel so long that, much as the captain regretted his daring and longed to heave her to, it would be unsafe to try and bring her up to the wind.

The old barque ran well; indeed, unlike most vessels, she was more comfortable when running before the wind than she was when hove-to, and her decks were fairly dry, except when she yawed and shipped a heavy sea over the rail. Two men were at the wheel, and the captain stood by them all night patiently conning the labouring vessel, and encouraging the busy perspiring helmsmen. At every relief of the wheel he cautioned the new-comers not to look astern, and truly to do so was to behold an unnerving spectacle. The long high Cape Horn combers, which have been estimated to run seven or eight to the mile, were sweeping up behind us with irresistible force, each one as it came on seeming as if it were towering high above our stern and just about to crash on board, overwhelm, and swamp us. Then the old barque would fling her stern jauntily into the air, and the crest of the monster wave would foam harmlessly along her side as she slid down its slope. None but the best and most stout-hearted men were allowed to the wheel, for had any of them faltered as one of those gigantic seas swept up astern and allowed it for an instant to get out on the quarter, we should certainly have broached-to. All that night as we flew before that shrieking gale and those furious towering seas we prayed God that no unseen outward-bounder was lurking, hove-to, in our path. It was only occasionally wholly dark. There was a full moon, but all we could see of it was the brighter patch in the sky over which the ragged clouds were tearing. Then a black squall of rain and sleet would come along, obscuring even the lofty masts and straining bands of canvas. During those squalls keeping a look-out was quite impossible.

Next forenoon the wind, with little warning except a sudden brightening of the horizon to the south and a quick rise of the barometer, flew around to the south-west, and eventually it moderated slightly. By four o'clock in the afternoon it became evident that, if the vessel were to be kept ahead of the pursuing waves, her speed must be increased, so at the change of the watch the captain gave orders to set the fore-sail. After a struggle with the wet, heavy, slatting canvas this was done, and we had just hauled taut the starboard sheet and belayed it, when unexpectedly the barque dipped her starboard rail under the water. Some of the men were thrown off their feet and found themselves washing about in the scuppers ; those of us who had managed to get hold of a life-line and hang on to it suddenly saw an oilskin-clad figure floating along outside the ship ; it was the boatswain.

" Man overboard ! The bo'sun overboard ! " we shouted.

Shouting as we went we ran aft, knowing in our hearts that our shouting was in vain. To bring the vessel to the wind prior to lowering a boat would be to court disaster, indeed now that the fore-sail was set it could not have been done at all in less than half an hour, by which time the boatswain, if still afloat, would have been five miles astern ; in any case no boat could live in that sea. Then the almost incredible happened ; the boatswain seemed to be making no attempt to swim ; he was floating, I believe, because of the air which was incased within his oilskins, these being tied by rope-yarns at his ankles and his wrists ; and just as he had almost reached the break of the poop, one of the seas which had come up astern and split, came foaming along, swirled him forward two or three yards, and washed him back on to the rail. Half a dozen of us made a rush and got hold of him, getting another ducking as the sea swept over us. The boatswain stood safely on the deck blaspheming, gasping, and wiping the water from his eyes. The captain had witnessed the whole affair.

"Here, you!" he shouted to me, "take the bo'sun into the pantry and tell the steward to give him a glass of grog."

Followed by envious eyes I did as directed, and went into the saloon to fetch the steward. The latter produced a bottle and filled a glass ; the bo'sun took off the contents of the glass with one swallow and smacked his lips. Then the old sailor's instinct for a growl was too much for him.

"The old man is openin' 'is 'eart all of a sudden, ain't he," he remarked. "givin' a man a glass o' grog becos he 'appens to get wet."

"Weel," replied the steward rather stiffly, for he never forgot that he belonged to the after-guard, "when a man's been overboard a dram tae steady his nerves is no' oot 'o the way."

"Who's been overboard?" queried the boat-swain, looking at me, and truth to tell I was just as wet and drenched-looking as he was.

"Why, you have," replied the steward.

"Me!" exclaimed the astonished boatswain, as still smacking his lips he made for the door, "it's the first I know about it."

The disgusted steward watched the boatswain depart, and I waited to hear what he would say. He was a dour Scotsman with whom, for some reason or other, I was rather a favourite.

"Weel," he said at last slowly, "if that's no'

perfectly priceless. A glass o' rum clean thrown away tae revive a man that didn't know he had been overboard. H'm! aye! aye! You look a bit damp yersel'. I've wasted one glass o' grog the day, I micht as weel waste anither. Here!"

The wind gradually took off, and setting sail after sail as it diminished we ran before it. By the following evening everything was set. We were east of the meridian of Staten Land, and had started to edge to the north. We were justified in thinking that, for the time being, our troubles were over. George certainly thought so, for that evening after he had hove the log, he lingered near the taff-rail and looked long over the stern at the rolling road that leads round Cape Horn. Then he took off his cap, bowed politely in the direction in which he thought that headland lay, and said—

" Good-bye! I never want to see you again."

About ten o'clock that same evening the wind was almost due south, and with it well on the star-board quarter we were doing about eight knots. We were in high spirits. As usual in those latitudes the watch on deck was hanging about the break of the poop ready to carry out any orders; above us the second mate was pacing fore and aft keeping his watch. It was now bitterly cold, and small wonder we thought, for the wind was blowing straight up from the ice-clad Antarctic continent. We stamped our feet and flapped our hands across our chests in the manner of a London cabby in a vain endeavour to get warm. We heard voices above us: the old man had just come up from below and joined the second mate.

" It's very cold, mister," we heard him remark.

" Yes, sir," replied the second, " and getting colder all the time."

A deep deliberate hail in a sonorous voice from the Dane, who was on the look-out on the forecastle head, came suddenly booming along the deck. It carried well above the sighing of the wind in the rigging.

" Dere vass sömedings on de vedder bow."

" All right," replied the second mate. Then he remarked to the captain—-

" There was something on the weather bow. That's a curious report, sir."

" It is," assented the old man. " Jump forward and see what it is."

Down on the main deck as the second mate passed through us on his way forward we chuckled. It *was* a curious report—not the short crisp one which is expected from the look-out man, and which we knew so well how to give.

" Less noise on the main deck there. Come up here some of you and brail in the spanker and haul down the gaff top-sail. Let them hang," the captain ordered. Then to the man at the wheel, " Let her go off a couple of points."

The second mate returned, and by that time the captain had got his binoculars and was peering out broad on the bow.

" There *is* something there, sir," said the former. " It can't be, of course, but it looks like a small island."

" I see it," was the reply. " Good God ! *ice.* Let her go right off."

Ice! No wonder it had been cold. We flew to carry out the orders to haul the yards round and to shorten sail, and very shortly, with little canvas set, we were head reaching on the port tack back in the direction from which we had just come. As the old man remarked, we knew that there was no ice there. At daybreak we hauled off to the north-east again with all sail set once more. First we saw a small berg like an islet, probably the one which we had seen the previous night. A mile beyond it was the main iceberg, from which it had probably broken away. This berg was about ten miles in length, and must have been over a hundred feet high. The side of it on which we passed appeared exactly like a pure white steep rocky coast, with a series of vertical cliffs and deep caves. Into these caves the waves ran foaming, or they would dash against the cliffs in columns of spray. It was really a magnificent spectacle although an entirely unwelcome one, a far more pleasing prospect being the stretch of open water to the north.

We steered in that direction, and soon cleared the main berg and a few smaller outlying ones beyond it. During the whole day a look-out was kept from the fore topgallant yard, and at sunset, as no further ice had been seen, the old man decided to carry on with everything set. We were now north of the latitude of the Horn and fast leaving it behind, running away toward flying fish weather again, steering for the well-known milestones which marked the progress of the homeward-bound windjammer. First, we would have the south-east trades, when it is good to be alive and knocking

about the deck bare-footed ; when a vessel may
stand on for days on end without touching brace
or sheet. Then would come the doldrums, the
north - east trades, the brave westerlies of the
Atlantic : a distant glimpse of the Azores known to
seamen as the Western Islands, soundings at the
mouth of the English Channel—then Home.

III. A MID-WINTER NIGHT.

During that last passage home as I stood on deck and looked aloft at the towering stretch of canvas and the complicated network of standing and running rigging, and thought of the mixed crews of various nationalities, some of them the scum of the ports, that manned our modern sailing ships, I sometimes wondered how in a few short months, if I passed my examination, I—still little more than a boy—could face the responsibility of keeping a watch as an officer. Could I act up to that ideal conception of myself as a sailing ship second mate which I had set up ? Could I face the varied situations—many of them likely to be created with alarming swiftness—and give instantly the correct orders, or would I be found wanting ? It is true that I might go into steam right away—that is what we all aimed at eventually,—but I wished to prove my manhood, to have had the experience of having been an officer in sail.

Like many big ship apprentices I would sometimes despair, but would then console myself with a compromise. Instead of one of those great, clumsy, undermanned brutes in which I had served my apprenticeship, what about a handy little barque—a three-masted one ? I duly passed my examination, and shortly afterwards, to my joy, was appointed second mate of as handy a little barque as ever sailed the ocean. There was one fly in the ointment of my contentment : she was loading in the Tyne for Valparaiso, which meant once again rounding the Horn, and this time in the dead of winter. However, handy little barques are not picked up every day, and I was a proud although rather an anxious man as I kept my first watch running down the North Sea.

Now we were drawing near to the Horn again. This time we had not been able to get through the Strait of Le Maire, but had passed to the east of Staten Land. It looked more bleak, more desolate than ever—snow-clad right down to the beach. That night I had the watch from eight to twelve, and a more perfect night I have rarely seen. The wind was from the south-east and moderate ; the air was cold and frosty, but it was as clear as a bell ; a full moon rode high along the lee beam with hardly a cloud passing over it. It was the 21st June—mid-winter day. With the wind two points abaft the beam, every sail was set and drawing, and the barque was gliding along in that noiseless manner characteristic of a sailing vessel in a moderate wind, leaning over steadily but not rolling, slipping through the smooth sea, the foam which her sharp bow had created from the tiny wavelets sparkling as it raced past her sides.

The lee sides of the sails gleamed white in the moonlight, the reverse sides of them were in shadow, and dark shadows were also cast on the clean dry decks and on the moonlit sea to windward. As I walked up and down the poop keeping a careful eye aloft for any shift of wind, scraps of subdued conversation would reach me from the sailors who were clustered on the main deck about the break of the poop. As was generally the case in that vicinity, their talk was mostly about bygone passages round Cape Horn.

"Once in one of them Swansea copper ore-men we 'ad a slant like this 'ere. Smart little barque she wos too—but a reg'lar little divin' bell. She went below the water when we got down to forty south on the Atlantic side, and come up again when we got up to forty south in the Pacific. Well, all day, right off the pitch of the 'Orn, we wos in company with one of them *Braes* of Greenock——"

"I knows 'em. 'Ungry gutted packets they was too."

"They wos—I've sailed in one of 'em. Well, that night—a night like this it wos too—down comes a squall, a reg'lar snorter—took the fore to'gallant mast out of 'er afore it wos finished."

They paused in their conversation and looked up toward the poop where I was keeping my watch. I felt that they were wondering if I was quite sure of what I was doing—carrying every stitch of canvas, even if the wind *was* steady and moderate, in a tract of water which is reputed to be about stormiest in the world. They would stare steadily to windward and then look aloft to where the tiny little royals, the lightest sails of all, clean full and bellying gracefully, were tugging lightly at their sheets. I verily believe that they looked upon it almost as sacrilege, this carrying of royals off the pitch of the Horn in the middle of winter. The watch wore on and I was left to keep it undisturbed ; the captain had gone below at nine o'clock after telling me to call him if the wind or the weather changed, and had not come up again. The wind remained steady in direction but increased ever so slightly ; when the apprentices hove the log at one bell—a quarter to twelve—the barque was doing seven and a half knots.

" *Din-ding, din-ding, din-ding, din-ding*," went the small bell on the poop ; " *Cla-clang, cla-clang, cla-clang, cla-clang*," answered the large one on the forecastle head ; then the mournful " *A-a-all's well*," long drawn out and sounded on one note, floated peacefully along the deck from the look-out forward. The mate came out of the companion way, and advanced, yawning heavily, to the forward end of the poop. Below us the men of both watches were silently mustering.

" Watch is aft, sir," the boatswain reported in soft drowsy tones.

" Relieve the wheel and look-out," replied the mate in an equally sleepy voice.

My watch on deck was over. I lingered for a little part of my precious watch below talking to the mate, who was an old Cape Horn hand, and asked him if he thought that this fair wind might last. He looked to windward carefully.

" I believe it will—touch wood," he replied, rubbing the palm of his hand along the teakwood rail, " and if it does, even for two days, we are as good as round."

I came on deck again at four o'clock. The moon was now well on the lee bow and considerably nearer the horizon, but apart from that there was no change. The wind had been steady throughout ; they had not touched a brace during the watch, the mate told me. And it held steady in direction, but increased until we were doing over ten knots, not for two days only but for another nine, and by the end of that time we did not care what it did, for we had reached our destination ; in ten days we had sailed two thousand miles—from the east side of Staten Land, round the Horn, and right into Valparaiso Harbour.

THE PILGRIM SHIP.

I.

BASRA ten years before the war was in very much the same state as our troops found it in when they first occupied it. There was the same maze of tortuous lanes ankle-deep in filth, the same total absence of sanitation, and the incredibly uninteresting bazaars with their mixed populations. Altogether it was an extremely dreary place in which to idle away ten days, and this was apparently what I was doomed to do.

I had just come down from the vicinity of Babylon, where I had been engaged in excavation work, and, owing to the Tigris being low, the river steamer on which I had travelled down to Basra had stuck on the shoals so frequently that I had missed the mail steamer to Bombay, from which port I had intended to sail to England. The brightest spot in Basra was the little club standing in the narrow lane between two mud walls, which many officers of the Expeditionary Force afterwards came to know so well; and I was sitting there one sultry evening when a man employed with one of the British mercantile firms, who knew my plight, came up to me.

" Look here," he said. " Why don't you go on to Aden instead of waiting for the mail steamer to Bombay ? It is the most direct route home in any case. A steamer has just arrived to take pilgrims to Jeddah, and I hear that she is calling at Aden. She may not be very comfortable perhaps, and she belongs to a native-owned line of no repute, but as it would certainly shorten your journey and also save you a long wait here, it might be worth your while."

It would have been more correct had my friend said that the native-owned steamer *Hormuz* belonged to a line of coasting steamers with rather a poor reputation. The steamers of the line were manned by natives and officered by Europeans, but many of the latter were merely certificated beach-combers. I had heard many amusing tales of their doings : one voyage a man would sail in command, but by the time that another voyage started he would be so incapable that he had to be discharged, the chief officer would replace him, and as likely as not, owing to the scarcity of certificated officers, the former skipper would go as chief officer. Who took command on the following voyage would depend to a great extent upon which of them could remain sober the longest. Much of this was due to the fact that the native owners were out to get the cheapest men whom they could procure, and I hasten to say that that state of affairs no longer exists ; in a world which is gradually becoming more sober the beach-comber officer has disappeared.

By this time I had completely exhausted the

few amenities of Basra, and, as my friend had pointed out, there were many advantages to me in being able to leave it at once and proceed straight to Aden. The next morning I visited Ashar, and called in at the office of the native agents to make inquiries. There I met the captain of the *Hormuz*. He was a very pleasant and courteous old gentleman, but he did not seem to be at all pleased at the idea of having me as a passenger, although he was much too polite to say so directly. He took me aside and pointed out that the vessel would be absolutely packed with native pilgrims, that his stewards were not used to waiting on Europeans, and that the voyage was certain to be a very unpleasant one. By this time, however, I had begun to rather like the old chap, and when I intimated to the native agents that I had made up my mind to go in the ship and was prepared to pay well for my passage, there was little further opposition.

The *Hormuz* was lying out in the stream, and was due to leave the following afternoon. About an hour before sailing time I pushed off to her with my kit in a *bellum*. I had some difficulty in getting up the gangway ladder and along the main deck to the saloon, and the two *kavasses* who had come off with me to help with my kit had a terrific struggle to get it to my cabin, for natives were swarming everywhere, and the din which they were making was ear-splitting. When I did reach the saloon, which was amidships, I was surprised to see how clean and commodious it was. The *Hormuz* was an old passenger steamer; she had evidently been well kept, and I had a very roomy cabin. The

ship's officers appeared at the moment to be too
busy to take much notice of me, but the butler and
saloon boys, who were clean and smart, were very
attentive, and gave me an excellent tea, after which
I went on deck to watch the vessel's departure.
Accompanied by an absolute babel from the hordes
on deck and their hundreds of friends, who were
alongside the ship in various kinds of small
craft, the anchor was hove up, the vessel turned
round, and we started down the palm-fringed
river.

At dinner, which was a very good one, I met the
mate, who was a second edition of the captain—
rather elderly, courteous, and refined,—and also
the chief engineer, a Scotsman from the county of
Fife, who lapsed occasionally into his native dialect.
My apprehension regarding the officers of the
Hormuz began to vanish ; seldom had I met more
delightful companions. Presently the mate went
up on the bridge to relieve the second mate, who
came into the saloon for his dinner. I took to the
latter at once : he was a tall, gentlemanly, young
fellow with a frank engaging smile, and I learned
that his name was Greatorex. He sat chatting
with the captain, chief engineer, and myself until
it was time for him to go on the bridge again, when
the little party broke up. The weather had been
very sultry on shore, but in her progress down the
river the vessel was making quite a nice breeze, so
that I had no trouble in getting to sleep in my
cabin.

The next day we were lying in the outer harbour
of Bushire in Southern Persia, where we had gone

to discharge the native pilot who had brought the ship down the Shatt-el-Arab, and also to take on board a few more boat-loads of pilgrims, though where these were going to be stowed away beat me, for the decks and 'tween-decks seemed already to be packed. There was no wind, the glassy waters of the harbour shimmered in the sun, and the white town of Bushire seemed to hang in a mirage between the blazing sky and the expanse of sandy beach. Eventually the occupants of the boats which had pulled off to us managed to manœuvre themselves up the gangway ladder, and to dissolve themselves in some mysterious manner amongst the other passengers, and we proceeded on our voyage.

As the vessel steamed slowly out of the harbour I looked around her with considerable interest. The officers' rooms, the saloon, the deck above it, which was reserved for Europeans, and the bridge, which rose above that again, seemed to stand up like an island in the middle of a sea of seething humanity. I could hardly have imagined it possible that so many human beings, with their bundles and belongings, could have been packed into such small spaces. They swarmed all over the decks forward and aft of the midship erection, which separated the two mobs, and the noise of their chattering and shouting was continuous. So close were they packed that the Lascars could only with difficulty push their way through them in order to do their various jobs about the deck. My cabin and the saloon were quite comfortable, and I had ample deck space in which to stretch my legs, but the close proximity of those two dense and ever-moving mobs, which seemed to hem us in, had at first rather an unnerving effect.

That evening after dinner I was walking on the saloon deck smoking a cigar, feeling slightly depressed, and rather wishing that the voyage were nearly over instead of just beginning, when at eight o'clock the second mate came off the bridge and joined me. There was a light following wind, with the result that the atmosphere was rather stifling.

" Come into my cabin," he said. " I think that with the electric fan it will be rather cooler there than it is on deck. There are only two of us, so that we have to keep watch and watch. That is why you see so little of us ; but I don't want to turn in much before nine."

I gladly assented, realising that the need for company was probably partly the cause of my depression, and he led the way to his cabin, pulled aside the curtain, and motioned me to go inside.

" I'll just tell one of the saloon boys to bring you a whisky-and-soda," he said. " You will excuse me if I don't join you, but I make a practice of not drinking at sea."

I entered the cabin. The door of a cupboard was open and swinging to and fro with the slight motion of the vessel, and as I closed it I noticed, lying over a peg, a slightly faded tie. This, in conjunction with a photograph in a frame, which was hanging on the bulkhead, gave me a clue.

" Were you at —— ? " I asked when he returned, naming my own public school.

" Yes, I was," he replied. " Why ? Were you ? "

We compared notes joyfully. I had left the term before he had gone to the school, but he, of course, knew most of the masters and many of the boys that I had known. We had plenty to talk about, and the time slipped past quickly. At last he had tactfully to remind me that he had to be on the bridge again at midnight, and I reluctantly rose from his settee, with an apology for keeping him up, and went on deck again. While I had been sitting in his cabin there had been no noise audible save that caused by the vibration of the engines, but as soon as I got into the open the hum of many human voices, now somewhat subdued but ever present night and day, came to me from both ends of the ship. I was now, however, feeling much more contented. Greatorex had been a great find, and I was longing for more of his company. Although I had seen little of the captain and the mate, I felt sure that I would find them very interesting when they had more time to devote to me. Greatorex had spoken well of both, and also of the chief engineer. The latter now joined me.

" Mister," he said, " it's a lang time atween drinks."

I agreed, and adjourned to *his* cabin, where we spent the remainder of the evening. I found out from him that the four whom I have mentioned were the only Europeans on board. All the other engineers and the doctor were educated natives. The chief produced a thing which he called a " dam brod," and his rather unsuccessful attempts to teach me how to play the game of draughts kept me interested and amused until it was time to go to bed.

II.

In all my experience of tropical countries I have never known heat to equal that which we endured the next day as the *Hormuz* steamed down the Persian Gulf. It was not like the clean heat of the desert, where there is generally a breeze. Here there was also a breeze, but, coming from right aft, it was blowing at a velocity which was about equal to the vessel's speed through the water, so that we retained the same oppressive atmosphere throughout the day, carried it along with us, and shared it with a thousand natives. The smoke from the funnel was rising straight up toward the zenith, while the smuts were dropping on the awnings like hail ; the gassy fumes from the stokehold mingled with the smell of stale oil from the engine-room ; the temperature seemed to be aggravated by the heat-retaining capacity of steel plates and by the furnaces below. I seemed to have no vitality. During the forenoon I lay on a deck-chair in the thinnest of clothing, hardly able to breathe, or moved slowly about the deck gasping like a fish that has just been taken out of the water.

Bad as the conditions were on deck, they were

much worse in the engine-room and stokehold, and I marvelled how men could exist and work there. I noticed that the vessel's speed through the water was gradually diminishing ; the men below were finding it impossible to keep a full head of steam. Although the chief engineer was down himself most of the day encouraging his men, for the greater part of the time the *Hormuz*, although her normal speed was eleven knots, was barely doing six. Occasionally one of the other engineers would come up to the engine-room door, sit down on the doorstep thoroughly exhausted, and endeavour to revive in the comparatively cooler air. I had often heard tales—what traveller hasn't ?—of stokers on vessels in the Red Sea becoming seized with sudden madness, rushing on deck, and throwing themselves overboard. Now I was quite prepared to believe them, and indeed expected something of the sort to happen. That it did not occur on board the *Hormuz* was mainly due to the chief engineer : he was much too experienced a Persian Gulf trader to be caught in that way. He had posted himself in the stokehold, and no stoker was allowed to leave it unless, having fainted, he was carried up into the alley-way, where one of the other engineers turned the hose on him, drenched him with water pumped from the sea, and watched him until he was able to resume his labours below. At one time I saw three of the stokers undergoing this treatment at the same moment, and all hands in the chief engineer's department were now on duty.

I had seen nothing of the captain or the officers

all day, and when I went into the saloon for lunch —not that I felt keen on eating anything, but because I was rather longing to speak to some one— I asked the butler about them.

"Captain and chief officer not having lunch, sir," he replied. "Second officer having lunch on bridge."

I managed a fitful doze in my long chair during the afternoon, but woke up bathed in perspiration in that Turkish-bath-like atmosphere. After tea I walked very slowly up and down the saloon deck, but avoided getting too close to either end of it, for from underneath the awnings which covered the decks below it there rose the odours which are naturally exuded by humanity confined, and perspiring, in such small spaces. The pilgrims were now, however, strangely silent. The temperature and the stifling conditions had proved too much even for them. The sun was getting lower, but the heat was not abating a single degree. As I strolled, Greatorex from the bridge saw me, and suggested that I might find it cooler up there.

"At any rate," he said, "you will be farther from that evil-smelling mob down on the main deck."

I went up the bridge ladder. It was the first time that I had been on the bridge, and I saw that it was a large and well-fitted one. At the after end of it was the chart-room, and, beyond that again, the captain's cabin. Just after I reached the bridge the captain's boy passed me with two bottles of soda-water, and after I had been talking to Greatorex for about ten minutes he appeared with two more and vanished into the cabin with them. Greatorex caught my eye.

"Look here," he said, "it's no use trying to hide it from you. These two old villains are drinking; that is why you haven't seen them all day."

"Good gracious!" I exclaimed, "who is doing the navigating and keeping the watches?"

"I am," he replied. "I don't mind; in fact I rather like it. Between ourselves this happens regularly once every voyage, and, although you may think it strange, I rather look forward to it. It is the only time that I have enough to do or have any real responsibility. They will be all right again in a couple of days."

"But you can't remain awake all that time."

"I don't need to. I have either the *serang* or the *tindal* up here on watch the whole time, and I sleep in that long chair. They have orders to call me every two hours, and instantly if they see a light or other vessel, and they have as good eye-sight as I have. We really manage quite nicely between us."

"I am surprised that you can put up with a pair of drunken wasters like that," I said, pointing toward the captain's cabin.

Greatorex looked at me, a curious smile on his face. "I am just as bad as they are," he said quietly, "only they never drink in port and I do. The words ' drunken waster ' really apply to me just as much as to them—that is why I am here."

He told me something of himself. He had served his apprenticeship in one of the well-known colonial clippers, and had been an officer in a crack line of mail and passenger steamers. Popularity with the passengers had really been his downfall. His head had got slightly swollen over it. When his first captain had remonstrated with him for drinking too much he had resented it. He had then been removed to another vessel, had gone from bad to worse, and was eventually dismissed from the service. It had all been his own fault, he assured me ; he had been given every chance. After that he had drifted out to the East, not caring very much what happened to him, and had been in various jobs. He had been in the *Hormuz* about eighteen months, and was, to a certain extent, happy and contented.

" She is the best ship in the company," he said, " in fact the only decent one. The old man and the mate have been in her for five years, and I don't believe that the owners know a single thing against them. I have a sort of working agreement with them : they can depend upon me running things at sea when they go off like this. To the owners I am just the usual rather dissipated but necessary second mate, and so long as the captain cares to carry me they don't mind. One feeds well here ; it's rather an easy job. Not a bad life really when one has lost all ambition."

" Yes, but it doesn't lead to anything."

" It leads to nothing that is any good," replied Greatorex grimly.

" Why do you take to drink when you get into port ? " I asked him.

" Nothing else to do," he replied promptly. " If you know anything of India, for instance, you will

realise that we people in ships like these are social
outcasts there. No one wants to know us, and
quite rightly. Some of the fellows get mixed up
with the women of the country—thank God I have
always avoided that,—others take to drink. I
am one of the drunkards."

"I cannot understand why, in a native-owned
ship like this, none of the crew give the captain and
mate away," I remarked.

"There's no fear of that," replied Greatorex.
"They have had the same deck and saloon crew
ever since they have been here, and the men love
them. They are such sahibs really, and no one
spots a gentleman quicker than a native. Besides,
they are quite harmless. If you went into that
cabin now you would find that they are talking
cricket; they are mad on it, both too old to play,
of course, but they follow it up, and read every
home paper they can get during the cricket season.
They never miss a match out here either if they can
manage to get to it. I am rather with them there.
I was in the eleven, you know."

"Of course you were," I replied, and understood
then why his name had been so familiar when I had
first heard it.

"The last time that we were in Bombay the
annual tournament was on, and the Europeans
were playing the Parsis. The three of us never
missed a ball during the whole three days, and in
the evenings we would come back on board, dress
for dinner—oh yes, we all have our glad rags—and
then go up to the Taj Mahal. We dined and wined
like gentlemen, did a show, and came back every

night perfectly sober. It was topping. Then I spoiled it. On the fourth day there was no cricket, and nothing else to do. In an evil moment I went ashore, met some low-down friends, and never saw daylight for three days. Excuse me a moment, I must fix her position before the sun sets, and lay off a good safe course for the night."

He went to the standard compass, took some bearings of the distant Persian hills, and laid them off on the chart. As he emerged from the chart-room the chief engineer came on the bridge and flopped down on a camp-stool. He was soaking as if he had just come out of the sea, and the perspiration was dripping off his trousers on to the deck.

" My God, this is awful ! " he gasped. " What aboot turnin' her roond now for a while ? "

" Right-o," said Greatorex, looking round the ocean to see that all was clear. " Hard-a-star-board, quartermaster. I will head her back for half an hour. I can't afford to go too far back at present, but if you put the engines at slow we won't lose so much ground, and besides, it will give you a chance to get the steam up."

" That'll dae fine," replied the chief.

As the *Hormuz* turned round sixteen points and swung head to wind we seemed to have suddenly entered another climate. The temperature fell, the revivifying air eddied and swirled through the ship, causing the awnings to flap, and the chief engineer seemed to be taking it down in great gulps. It brought the hordes of pilgrims to life, and they gave vent to howls of delight. Poor devils, they did not understand that it was only temporary and due to an alteration in the course ; they were greeting it as one greets the breaking of the monsoon in Bombay, or the bursting of the *shamal* in Basra. I could hardly have credited the fact that the simple manœuvre could have made such a difference, and remarked to Greatorex that it was a wonder that the chief engineer hadn't asked him to do it before.

" We discussed it several times," he said, " but just before you came up on the bridge we passed some nasty reefs that I was anxious to get clear of before dark." I gathered that those reefs were quite unmarked ; indeed at that time there wasn't a lighthouse in the Gulf or along the desolate Arabian coast between Muscat and Aden.

" Ye'll keep her like this for hauf an hoor, will ye ? " said the chief. " I'll gae doon an' see if I can get the steam up."

" Good chap, the chief," remarked Greatorex as that worthy disappeared from the bridge.

" Does he drink too ? " I asked, in a mildly sarcastic tone.

The second mate smiled. " He allows himself a bottle of whisky a day," he replied, " but I have never seen him turn a hair. Although we are all the best of friends, and he likes us, I fancy that he rather despises us too. He looks upon both tee-totalers and drunkards as weaklings."

Although I am not a particularly nervous man, I must confess that I did not sleep very much that night, for, apart from the heat, I could not help thinking of the *Hormuz*, with her huge freight of human souls, ploughing on through the night with at times only a *serang* or *tindal* on watch. I had full faith in Greatorex, who appeared to be wholly competent and full of confidence, but I doubted his ability to keep alert night and day. That he was awake part of the night was evident, for on at least two occasions the *Hormuz* was again turned head to wind. The cooling breeze which swept in through the wind-shoot which protruded out of the port-hole of my cabin was entirely different to the much-breathed atmosphere which the blades of the electric fan had been merely disturbing. Truly I was having a rather curious voyage.

III.

The next morning it was rather cooler : the wind
had gone round abeam, and after breakfast, when
I went up on the bridge, I found Greatorex looking
quite fresh. Just after sunrise, the vessel being on
a safe course and there being nothing in sight, he
had taken the opportunity to go below for a bath
and a shave, and now, clad in a clean white suit,
he was cheerfully humming a song. We had been
chatting for some time, when there came to our
ears a strange noise from the deck below. It seemed
entirely different to the usual drone, punctuated by
shouts, of the pilgrims—it sounded more like a
dirge. The *serang*, who was on watch on the bridge
at the time, walked forward to the rail and listened
intently. Then he said suddenly in the Lascari
bât—

" Many of the passengers have died, sahib."

Before Greatorex could investigate this rather
startling statement, a native precipitated himself
on to the bridge, and stood before us trembling
violently. It was the ship's doctor.

" I want to see the captain, sir, at once, instantly," he shouted excitedly.

" Well, I am afraid that you can't," lied Greatorex

calmly. " He has been on the bridge all night, and
he is now lying down. What's the matter ? "

" My God, sir, it is cholera ! " replied the doctor.

" The devil it is," said Greatorex. " Have there
been many deaths ? "

" An appalling quantity, sir, appalling," moaned
the doctor. " The situation is most terrifying."

" The first effect of this," said the second mate,
after he had succeeded in slightly calming the
thoroughly frightened doctor, and sent him away
to look after his job, " will be that these two old
gentlemen will have to curtail their—er—holiday."

" But will they stop drinking ? " I asked him
anxiously.

" Rather," he replied. " I'll fix them."

He left me and went into the captain's cabin. I
have no idea what methods he used, but a few hours
afterwards the captain was looking after the
navigation and the mate was keeping his watch on
the bridge, and I never saw either of them touch
liquor during the rest of my time on board. Two
rather serious things, however, happened during
the day. The first was that the little doctor
trembled himself to death—it is about the only
way that I can describe it. He certainly took
more than his share of the scanty stock of cholera
medicine which was on board, but I am convinced
that it was terror more than an overdose of chloro-
dine that finished him. The second thing was that
the crew absolutely refused to handle the corpses
which were lying about in the 'tween-decks, nor
would the other passengers touch them. With
true fatalism these men who were making the

pilgrimage merely shrugged their shoulders when appealed to, sat on their praying-mats, and chanted recitations from the Koran.

" Isn't the captain rather weak that he can't compel the crew to do it ? " I asked Greatorex rather indignantly. " Some skippers that I have read about would have been among them before now."

" What ? The hard case bucko skipper, knuckle-dusters, gun play, and that sort of thing," he replied with a laugh. " Not a bit of good. It might do with some crews, but these fellows would only get mulish, then silly, and probably wind up by dying too. No, as far as I can see, *I* will have to go down and send up the remains of the deceased."

I was permitted to be present at a conference held on the bridge between the Europeans on board, when it was decided that that was the only way. The others, however, insisted that Greatorex must be heavily doped with brandy as a preventive before he started, and they made no mistake about it. For the next three days the captain and mate had to keep *his* watch between them ; he was never sober, and really I could hardly wonder at it. Indeed I felt almost glad that he *was* that way when I first saw him go down the hatch, through that seething mob, and into the 'tween-deck below with its foul, breath-catching atmosphere, composed of the exhalations of many natives, and the sour smell of sweaty garments long unwashed. To make matters worse, the 'tween-deck was now more crowded than ever ; the *Hormuz* was by this time in the Arabian Sea, plunging into the monsoon, and throwing spray all over the fore-deck. It was impossible to keep the pilgrims from huddling below, where they were still dying at the rate of a dozen a day. With the motion of the vessel many of them were also sea-sick.

Twice a day, morning and evening, Greatorex performed his gruesome task. He had to grope about in the semi-dark, ignorant of any language which the pilgrims understood, find the corpses, and then drag them to the square of the hatch. There he would pass a rope-sling round the body and hook on the derrick fall. The chief engineer was at the winch, and on the signal being given he hove the corpse out of the hatch ; the mate and the Chinese carpenter manned the derrick guy and hauled the derrick over till it plumbed the deck close to the side where part of the bulwark had been let down on a hinge as if for working cargo. The engineer walked back the winch and landed the corpse on that part of the bulwark which was now lying flat on the deck, the carpenter removed the sling, and he and the mate rolled the body into the sea.

One evening I stood on the saloon deck, underneath the bridge, watching the bodies being hove out of No. 2 hatch. The weather, on deck at least, was now fairly cool, although it must still have been hot and stuffy in those horrible 'tween-decks. There was a fresh breeze, the sky was overcast with clouds which completely obscured the sun, and the monsoon waves were a slaty colour, with curling white tops. The awning had been removed to allow the derrick to swing freely, so that I could see right down the hatch into the 'tween-deck. The chief engineer had just hove up a body, and before the others could pull the derrick over, he lowered the body swiftly on to the deck.

" What's the matter, chief ? " asked the mate in surprise.

" Matter ! " cried the chief, shutting off the steam from the winch and striding toward the others, " that man's no' deid."

It was perfectly true. The man's eyes were opening and closing ; he was twisting his body as well as he could in the sling, and moving his hands.

" Here, Greatorex," the mate roared down the hatch.

" Hullo ! " came from the deck below.

" Go easy, my lad ; that last man you sent up wasn't dead."

Greatorex stood swaying in the square of the hatch and blinking up at the sky.

" What the hell is the odds," he yelled with drunken bravado, " he very soon will be."

The next morning, just before the performance was due to be repeated, I walked forward along the saloon deck, and found Greatorex—looking rather white about the gills, but perfectly sober— sitting at a small table with the chief engineer and the mate standing over him. The latter had a bottle of brandy in one hand and a tumbler in the other, and was evidently trying to induce the second mate to drink. The captain was watching the proceedings from the bridge above, and as I arrived on the scene he shouted—

" What's the matter down there ? It is about time you started, before it gets too hot."

" Greatorex won't take his medicine, sir," replied the mate, shaking his head solemnly and again placing the brandy bottle prominently on the table. The young officer pushed it away with a gesture of disgust, and the chief engineer chimed in—

" Look here, mister, think o' yer shipmates," he said. " Suppose that a cholera bug happens tae bite *you*, what are we gaun t' dae ? The mate's ower auld to gang doon there and haul corpses aboot, I hae the winch tae drive, and my Aryan brither engineers 'll no' face it. Think o' yer shipmates and tak' yer dram like a man."

" I will not drink any more of the stuff," declared Greatorex decisively. " In any case I have enough brandy in my system now to kill every damned cholera microbe on board the ship."

Later on, after the morning performance was over and he had bathed and shaved, the second mate confided in me—

" I woke up this morning feeling like nothing on earth," he said ; " remembered where I was, and reached for the brandy bottle. Then I suddenly asked myself why the devil I was drinking the stuff. Of course, I started off taking it with the idea that it would defeat the germs, but it wasn't for that reason that I was going to take it this morning. No, it was to give me the necessary pluck to go down the hatch. I said to myself, ' By Gad, if I have to take brandy to give me Dutch courage to face a job like that, I *have* sunk pretty low,' so I made up my mind that I would not touch another drop. It's a rotten job, all the same," he continued, shivering slightly. " There were fourteen corpses to be got out this morning, and I felt very sorry for myself several times before I finished. I'll manage to stick it, though."

To the great relief of every one on board, we arrived at Aden two days afterwards, with Great-orex, despite the forebodings of the others, still alive. The pilgrims were removed to the quarantine station, the vessel thoroughly disinfected, and after a few days I was allowed to go on shore. I had not long to wait in Aden. A large mail steamer was due from Australia the next day, and I booked my passage to England on her. She arrived early in the morning. I sent off my baggage, and decided to call on board the *Hormuz*—both vessels were lying off in the roads—on my way off to her, ostensibly to say good-bye to those on board, but really to work a little scheme which I had planned. I make no pretensions to being a social reformer, and usually I believe firmly in minding my own business, but I had taken a great liking to Great-orex, and hoped that our friendship would not be the usual short-lived one that is so often formed aboard ships. I thought that a glimpse of the sort of life which he used to lead, and a comparison between it and that which he was leading now, might tend to rekindle his lost ambition and urge him to pull himself together. The mail steamer was not sailing until 4 P.M.—I would ask him to come on board of her and have lunch with me.

He was in his cabin reading when I went on

board, but he seemed to hesitate when I made my proposal.

"That isn't the line that you were an officer on, is it?" I asked him.

"Oh, no," he replied. "I don't suppose that any one there will know me. Right, thanks very much. I'll come. You go up and speak to the old gentlemen while I change."

I found the captain and the mate lying comfortably in long chairs and surrounded by piles of English newspapers. They were perfectly happy, piecing together over by over a match that had been played at Lords a month before. The chief engineer was doing some job below, but a hail brought him up to the engine-room door to bid me adieu.

"Good-luck tae ye, mister," he said, squeezing my hand in his large and grimy paw; "this ought tae learn ye a lesson. Ye'll think twice afore ye tak a passage in a pilgrim ship again."

I could have told him, but refrained, that I had made a resolution some time ago to the effect that I would *never* take such a passage again. Greatorex came up on the saloon deck just then, and when I saw him in a tussore silk suit, with the slightly faded school tie which he had doubtless put on as a compliment to me, and his solar *topi* with smart puggari round it, I could not help reflecting what an eminently presentable young fellow he looked. The old gentlemen came along to the gangway with us, bade me farewell, and wished me *bon voyage* with old-time courtesy. As the boat was pulling away with us, I saw them hurrying back to their newspapers, and knew that in ten minutes' time I would be out of their minds for ever, whereas C. B. Fry, or whoever happened to be scoring centuries at the time, would remain in them for a long time.

At lunch in the first-class saloon of the liner, Greatorex, quite at his ease, sat between me and a very pretty Australian girl, and seemed to thoroughly enjoy her company. Poor devil! she was probably the first lady that he had conversed with for years. Afterwards they strolled about the deck for a little while, as I had some business to attend to in my cabin. At last orders came for all those not sailing in the ship to go ashore. I walked along the deck with him, our hands met in a steady grip, and as I watched his tall figure running lightly down the gangway ladder and stepping into the waiting boat, I wondered where, if ever, I should meet him again.

IV.

During the next few years whenever my various duties took me to the East, and I visited such places as the Eastern Exchange in Port Said, the G.O.H. in Colombo, and the Taj Mahal in Bombay, where men congregate, I made inquiry for Great-orex, but in vain, and sometimes feared that he might have gone under altogether, as Europeans sometimes do in the East. Then came the war, and for four years I was rather busy on the Continent. After that he gradually began to fade from my memory until I met him again last year—of all places in my own club in Town.

I recognised him almost at once, for he had changed very little either in face or figure. I rose and went toward him with outstretched hand. He took it hesitatingly, looked straight into my face, and then said politely—

" You will forgive me for not remembering your name. You see I carry so many passengers during the course of a year that—— Good Lord, *you*, after all these years. This is the sort of meeting that makes work for the barman. Here, Harris," to the smoking-room waiter, " two whiskies-and-sodas, please."

We sat down at a small table and fairly beamed at each other. It was a joy to me to see his general air of prosperity and well-being. " Now tell me all about yourself," he insisted.

I would rather that it had been the other way, but my modest story was soon completed, and I then listened eagerly to his. He had gone back to the ship and done some solid thinking, and decided to give himself another chance in life. For a year he remained on in the *Hormuz*, saving money to come home and make a fresh start. When he arrived in England he found that he still had one or two influential friends. He had got into one of the large Atlantic lines as a junior officer, got his first command during the war, and was now in one of the company's largest vessels.

" And what about this ? " I asked after a time, pointing to his half-empty glass. I felt that I knew him well enough to put the question without giving offence.

Greatorex laughed merrily. " For two years after you left Aden I went strictly on the water waggon," he said. " I did it in the first place to help me to save money to get home, and I kept it up in my new job because I was rather frightened to chance taking a drink. Then when I saw the other fellows round me enjoying themselves in moderation, I remembered the old chief's ideas about teetotalers and drunkards, and started in very cautiously ; now I just drink normally the same as other people. I know my capacity, and work accordingly. I haven't been tight since, although," with a reminiscent twinkle in his eye,

" I was precious near it after we heard that the Armistice had been signed. We were doing transport work at the time, and were lying in Alexandria. Like a lot of other men, I keep up my old practice of never drinking at sea, and brandy I *never* touch ; the very smell of it sends my thoughts back to the 'tween-decks of the *Hormuz*."

" I suppose you have heard nothing of your old shipmates since you left her," I said.

" Yes, rather," he replied. " I see the two old gentlemen occasionally. They only lasted one voyage after I left them : the new second mate let them down badly, and they were pushed out. Luckily for them it didn't matter very much, for the old skipper came into a whole lot of money just at the time. They came home, and have been living together in a house out Hampstead way ever since. They were looking a bit frail, though, when I saw them last ; it was in the Tube one morning last summer. They were on their way to the Oval."

THE *MAID OF MIRAMICHI*.

I.

WITH the reasons which induced the ex-naval officer who stood at tide-time on the dock wall of the tidal basin of Barry Docks near Cardiff, to take a pierhead jump on the Nova Scotia owned full-rigged ship *Maid of Miramichi*, this story is not concerned. Neither is it concerned with the methods by which he had obtained the able-seaman's discharge note from the barque *Gleaner* of London which he had in his pocket, and by means of which he intended to get a berth on board of the Nova Scotiaman, and indeed those methods would not bear very strict investigation. The discharge note was in the name of William Jackson, it was marked 'V.G.' in the two circles provided upon it for the purpose, thus indicating that during the previous voyage of the *Gleaner* both the ability and conduct of its owner had been very good, and of a necessity it was under the name of William Jackson that its present bearer must ship. Beside 'William Jackson' on the quay wall there stood a young Japanese sailor who was also waiting to take a pierhead jump on the Nova Scotiaman. The men, physically, were worthy representatives of their respective races—the Englishman a couple of inches under six feet, the Japanese the same number of inches over five. Both were powerfully built and muscular—the Englishman lithe and sinewy, the Japanese stocky and broad. The discharge note, which was of a recent date, gave the age of William Jackson as thirty, which was just about correct for the present holder of it. With them, for the purpose of shepherding them on board, was a Board of Trade official from the Shipping Office, who had brought them down in response to an urgent message from the master of the *Maid of Miramichi* to the effect that, despite all the efforts of boarding-house masters and crimps, his vessel was still two hands short of the crew which had signed on the previous day.

A fresh south-west breeze was blowing up from the Bristol Channel that morning in early December bringing with it a fine drizzle, and William Jackson —who was holding on to a well-filled white canvas bag with his right hand, while over his left arm there hung a straw mattress familiarly known to sailors as a ' donkey's breakfast '—shivered in his thin blue dungaree suit. They had not long to wait now, the bow of the *Maid of Miramichi* was entering the basin from the dock. Presently they were joined by another seaman—he was the boatswain of a tramp steamer which was coming out of the dock after the full-rigged ship, he said.

" Signin' on aboard that ' blue-nose,' matey ? " he asked affably.

" Yes," replied William Jackson.

" Gawd 'elp yer," said the boatswain solemnly.

He was inclined to be conversational. No more

of those Cape Horners for him, he said. Not likely. He had " knocked off the sea and gone into steam- boats " long ago. To the Mediterranean with coal, then up the Black Sea for wheat—that was his routine ; three months' voyages and long enough too. He looked solid, well-fed, and contented.

Certainly the *Maid of Miramichi* did not present a very promising spectacle to a seaman's eye, de- spite her lofty spars which seemed to tower above everything else in the dock, for she carried three sky-sail yards. She was built of soft wood and painted black ; her lines were pleasing, but at the moment she looked like a hulk, for her high flaring bow was disfigured by her jib-boom which had not yet been rigged out, but which lay on top of the bowsprit, so that she appeared to be blunted for- ward, and the tangle of stays and guys around it almost suggested a wreck. Overhead, masts and spars were black with coal dust, and as she was slowly warped into the basin they could see that her decks, deck-houses which had been painted white, and fittings were in the same condition. On the main-deck everything was chaos. William Jackson shivered again ; there was something for- bidding about this black sombre-looking vessel on board of which he was destined to sail, and he mentally contrasted her with the trim naval vessels to which hitherto he had been accustomed. Pre- ceded by the Board of Trade official and followed by the Japanese, he stepped from the quay wall on to the rail, and from there dropped on to the main- deck still grasping his canvas bag and ' donkey's breakfast.' They were hailed from aft by a tall,

lanky, sour-looking man, with a goat-like beard—
her captain,—who ordered them into the saloon.
On arrival there he eyed them cynically, passed
over William Jackson, and transferred his gaze to
the Japanese.

"Hell," he growled to the official, "is this the
best yew kin do?"

"It is," replied the Board of Trade man indifferently. "Your vessel don't exactly appear to
be popular, captain, but, in any case, those Japs
get a good name as sailormen."

"Aall right," replied the captain with a sneer,
"git on with the business and let's git to sea."

The 'articles'—the form of agreement between
the master and his crew—lay on the cabin table;
the official picked them up and read over the printed
matter which they contained, but so rapidly did
he read, and so much did he garble his words, that
beyond the fact that the vessel was bound to San
Francisco and anywhere that she cared to go afterwards, and that he would be paid off on her return
to the United Kingdom, or failing that, at the end
of three years, William Jackson did not understand a word. However, glad to get the farce over,
he signed his adopted name in two places, and his
doom for the present was sealed. The Board of
Trade man copied the name of the Japanese from
his discharge, as he had done the other, then made
a cross in the next column.

"Here, touch the pen," he said.

"I'll sign my name," replied the Jap with
dignity. He took the pen and wrote—in clear
letters—W. Kuroki.

The captain fixed them with a cold stare from his piercing steel-blue eyes.

" Git for'ad naow as quick as hell will let you an' turn to ! " he snarled.

They proceeded along the littered main-deck toward the forecastle which was to be their future home, and had almost reached it when they received a reminder that they were expected to start work without delay. A stentorian voice hailed them from the forecastle head ; it belonged to the mate, and its tone resembled the bellowing of a bull.

" Here, yew two," he bawled, " git in there an' stow away yer dunnage. If yew ain't up here in two minutes I'll be along after yew, so yew'd best look lively ! "

" We had better do as he suggests, old chap," remarked Kuroki pleasantly, " otherwise there's likely to be trouble."

They entered the forecastle, which was right in the eyes of the ship, and a gloomy den it looked. A double row of bunks ran along each side—otherwise it was entirely devoid of furniture. The floor was strewn with bags, sea-chests, and bedding. Lying with his head on a bag was one of their future shipmates, so drunk that even the man-driving mate had been unable to make any impression upon him. Finding two vacant bunks side by side they deposited their bags and straw mattresses in them, then hurried out into the open air again, and climbed up the ladder on to the forecastle head. The last mooring rope had just been let go from the quay wall, the tug ahead had taken the strain of the hawser, and an ever-widening lane of water was forming between the ship and the shore. On the forecastle head was gathered the majority of the crew, and a motley lot they were—one negro, several Britishers in varying stages of intoxication, most of the remainder Scandinavians, with a couple of Italians. Towering above every one and all-pervading was the mate, six feet four if he was an inch, broad in proportion and powerfully built—a veritable giant. His features were hard; at a glance Jackson could see brutality stamped all over his red weather-beaten face. He was evidently a hustler—most ' blue-nose ' mates had that reputation—and at the moment, amid a hurricane of profanity, he was pushing the undisciplined rabble about in an endeavour to get the operation of rigging out the jib-boom started. There was considerable reason in his anxiety to get on with the job. In a very short time the vessel would be pitching into the south-west swell of the Bristol Channel, and, until the jib-boom was rigged out and secured in its place, the head-stays which supported the fore topmast and top-gallant mast could not be hove down and made fast. The heel-rope had just been doubled and led to the capstan, the bars of which had been shipped, and the mate was pushing some of the hands toward them when a Cockney able-seaman, who was at least half drunk, remonstrated—

" 'Ere, 'oo the 'ell are ye shovin' ? " he queried.

In complete astonishment the mate gazed at him for a moment ; then his great hand shot out, and, grabbing the Cockney by the throat, he shook

him as a housemaid shakes a duster, then flung
him on the deck. But the Cockney was game.
Rising to his feet, he squared up to the astonished
officer, and danced about on his toes in the ap-
proved manner of some boxing establishment in
the Blackfriars Road. He could evidently use his
fists, but his knowledge availed him little. The
mate had a length that was nearly twice his own,
and with a terrific drive he got the Cockney full
in the face ; the latter dropped on the deck, blood
pouring from his nose and mouth.

" Orl right," he spluttered in tones of submission,
" I've 'ad enough."

The mate stooped down, dragged the seaman to
his feet, and drew back his fist as if about to repeat
the doze ; then probably reflecting that if he did
he would be a man short in getting out the boom,
he shoved the Cockney against a capstan bar.

" Heave then, yew scum ! " he roared.

Considerably impressed and subdued, the hands
trudged round the capstan, their feet slipping in
slime, composed of coal dust, rain, and blood from
the Cockney and another sailor, who had also felt
the weight of the mate's enormous fist. Their
melancholy silence was broken by the tug's steam
whistle, which suddenly emitted a series of short
sharp blasts, those being reinforced by indignant
shouts and sarcastic remarks about steering, from
her crew. The *Maid of Miramichi* had sheered so
heavily that the tug was broad off on the bow, and
heading away almost at right angles to the ship.
The captain's voice, carried from aft by a megaphone, rose above the noise.

"Send two men along to the wheel here," he shouted; "these two swine are drunk."

"Blue hell!" roared the exasperated mate, "when *will* I get this blasted boom out? Here yew," he continued, singling out William Jackson, "kin yew steer?"

"Yes, sir," replied that able-seaman promptly.

"Waal, lay along aft to the wheel and take that yellow dwarf with you."

Very thankful to be out of the turmoil on the forecastle head, the two men made their way aft, passing, on the main-deck, the only officer with whom they were not yet acquainted, the second mate, who, with two or three of the most sober of the hands, was reeving off some of the running gear. He also was a powerfully built giant, but he was young, and had an open good-natured face. William Jackson rather thought that he would like him. They took up a position on either side of the wheel, the men whom they relieved being helped off the poop and on the road toward sobriety by the ready boot of the captain. The new helmsmen found the vessel yawing heavily, and it took them some little time to steady her; when they did, they received orders to keep the tug-boat dead ahead—to follow in her wake. It had been many years since William Jackson had steered a vessel, and that had been a picket-boat when he was a snotty. He had never steered a sailing vessel in his life with the exception of a ship's cutter, but it was evident that it was he whom the captain was depending on. He had the sense, however, to leave to Kuroki the inspiring of the movements of the wheel, and the Japanese did not let him down. The tug-boat, dancing to the head swell, remained right ahead in a position about fifty yards in front of the jib-boom, which was now rapidly being secured in its proper place.

About two o'clock, the jib-boom having at last been rigged out and stays and guys set up and made fast, all hands were sent to dinner. They weren't allowed long for the meal, for there was still much to be done, and the mate was eager to get at it. Jackson and Kuroki were relieved when the men came on deck again, but had barely time to gulp a few mouthfuls when they found themselves in demand once more; the men who had relieved them had not suited either, and soon they had their eyes glued again on the straining, jumping tug ahead. By four o'clock daylight of the short December day was beginning to fade ; Lundy Island was still some distance ahead, but the captain decided to get the canvas on her before dark. The tug-boat was ordered to haul off to the north ; men crawled up the rigging and out on to the yards ; fore and aft sails began to creep up the stays, and square-sails to be sheeted home, or yards hoisted ; the vessel began to heel over. All hands under the mates were sweating hard at sheets and halliards. William Jackson, heaving at the wheel, while deploring the brutality which he had witnessed but which he hoped was only temporary and due to the exceptional circumstances, could not but marvel at the manner in which those hard-driving officers had evolved order from chaos. Only that morning, before the vessel had hauled out of the docks and

C 2

while it was still dark, a mob of undisciplined men, total strangers, the scum of the port of Cardiff, half of them drunk, had descended on the ship which aloft and below was in the usual state of confusion caused by weeks in harbour, followed by rapid loading at the coal tips. Now, by their co-ordinated efforts, the vessel was capable of making progress under her own sail without the help of the tug. The tow-rope was cast off, the tug-boat sheered away, her men hauling in the hawser, and presently the *Maid of Miramichi*, under a cloud of canvas, was standing off on the port tack seeking an offing. The long voyage round Cape Horn to California had commenced in earnest. It could not possibly be accomplished in much less than four months, it would probably take five, and might easily take six, and during the whole of that time, with the possible exception of some desolate headland near the most southerly part of South America, they would never even get a glimpse of land. The lights on Lundy Island blinking through the rain gave them farewell.

II.

Three weeks afterwards a completely transformed *Maid of Miramichi* was running down
through the north-east trades. Gone was every
external sign that she had ever been in a coal port
and loaded a cargo there. Her decks, deck-houses,
and bulwarks had been scrubbed and scoured until
they were spotless ; her brasswork glistened from
constant burnishing ; indeed no man-of-war or
yacht could have been cleaner or presented a more
pleasing appearance than she did. Aloft, running
and standing gear and rigging had been overhauled,
every block and runner was working smoothly in
readiness for the shifting winds of the doldrums or
the hard weather farther south.

All this had been the result of continual work
and drive. Unlike the more easy-going English
ships there was no afternoon watch below on a
' blue-nose,' which meant that the men who had
had two spells of four hours below the previous
night were kept on deck all the next day and would
then have only four hours below the following night,
and all the time that they were on deck they were
driven hard by their relentless taskmasters.

William Jackson by this time had had the opportunity of getting acquainted with his shipmates, and with a few exceptions they had not grown upon him. The captain and mate were, frankly, tyrants, the former mainly with his tongue, which was bitter and cutting; nor did he abstain altogether from using a belaying-pin on any unfortunate seaman who disturbed his morose and sullen temper. The mate's tyranny was more active—not a day passed but some one in his watch felt the weight of his mighty fist. No one dared to look awry at either of them much less complain, and their merciless discipline had produced a humble submissiveness in all hands, which was combined with a nervous urge to jump to carry out any order that was issued. Both of those men hated sailormen before the mast—the 'mules' they called them— with a deadly hatred, for which perhaps there was some little excuse. They had served as young officers in a hard school, the Western Ocean packet ships, where they had to deal with crews of packet rats—the hardest, vilest, and most reckless men who sailed the seas. The captain was a 'downeaster' from the State of Maine, the mate a purebred 'blue-nose.' The second mate, in whose watch Jackson and Kuroki had found themselves when the watches had been picked at eight o'clock the first night at sea, was of a different type. Although he had also been brought up in a hard school, that of Nova Scotia sailing ships, he was a gentleman. Rumours had reached the forecastle, through the steward, that his father was part owner of the vessel, and that he was qualifying to command her. Although he could on occasion use his fists on a loafer or hanger-back just as well as the mate could, there was no brutality in his disposition, and there was a belief in the forecastle that he did not approve of the conduct of his superiors, although, of course, he never showed any sign of his disapproval. He also was an American—from Massachusetts.

In hard-case American and Nova Scotian ships it was the usual custom to form what was called an afterguard, the more effectively to keep the crew in submission and to cope with any attempts at disturbance. In addition to the officers, this afterguard was composed of all the petty officers, such as the boatswain, boatswain's mate, sailmaker, and carpenter. On board of the *Maid of Miramichi*, however, no such combination had been formed, for the officers—each man a giant— relied on their own powers, and the petty officers were treated in almost the same way as were the men. One precaution was taken—the first morning at sea all hands were paraded and ordered to produce the sheath-knives which every sailor carried ; these had their points broken off by the carpenter before being returned to their owners.

Amongst the forecastle hands there were few who interested William Jackson. In his own watch there was Kuroki, and the acquaintance which he had made with the young Japanese on the dock wall of the tidal basin at Barry Dock had ripened into friendship—perhaps the only real one which existed on board. Kuroki came of a good family in Japan. He had been for two years in a naval school there, had spent two years on the *Conway*, and a further three years as an apprentice on an English sailing ship. This accounted for the good English which he spoke. His intention was to proceed back to Japan, where he hoped to get on rapidly in the mercantile fleet which that country was at the time developing, but before doing so he was out for more experience. With the exception of William Jackson, who had been profoundly ignorant of the customs which obtained on merchant vessels, Kuroki was probably the only sailor on board of the ship who was there from choice ; the others, in debt to the boarding-house masters of Cardiff, had been obliged to take whatever berth first offered. He was well aware that ' blue-nose ' officers had the reputation of being brutal disciplinarians and hard drivers, but he also knew that no finer seamen sailed the seas, and he was willing to undergo any hardship in his insatiable pursuit after knowledge. Light-hearted, always smiling, ready to take anything that came along, he was a comforting companion to the ex - naval officer.

There was one other in the starboard watch whom William Jackson liked and trusted, and that was the boatswain's mate, a big, red-headed, taciturn Scotsman from north of the Forth. Although that petty officer was berthed separately from the crew, and kept very much to himself, he occasionally found a chance to have a yarn with Jackson in the second dog-watch. He was a fine seaman who feared no man, and got on well with the second mate, who quickly discovered his worth. In the

port watch there were two men to whom Jackson
was attracted, and, strangely enough, one of them
was Bert Hawkins, the Cockney who had stood up
to the mate on the day the ship left port. Un-
deniably vulgar, rather foul-mouthed, a man who
had never had a home but who had dodged about
London as a street Arab until he had been old
enough to go to sea, his wits sharpened by a continual fight for existence, he yet appealed to the
ex-naval officer, who liked him for his ready wit,
his cheeriness under all circumstances, and his
staunchness to any one whom he considered a
friend. The other man in the port watch was old
Alphonse—a Belgian,—a simple gentle creature
with a pair of childish blue eyes and a patient smile.
For the boatswain who led the port watch neither
Jackson nor any one else on board had much use.
He was a man who would cringe to the mate, make
a show of bullying the men when on deck, and yet
crawl after them during their watch below.

The attitude of the forecastle crowd toward
William Jackson may be summed up as one of
respect. They realised that he was a man of educa-
tion—' college bred ' some of them called him,—
but made no attempt to inquire into his past, about
which he was entirely reticent, even to Kuroki.
He was active and used to discipline, one of the
first to jump to carry out an order no matter how
distasteful the task might be, and his young officer
had rather taken a fancy to him. So far neither he
nor Kuroki had felt, or needed, the incentive of
kick or blow.

" A toff wot's dahn on his luck, that's wot 'e is,"
was the summing up of Bert Hawkins. " I wos
shipmates once wiv one somefink like 'im—bin an
orfficer in the P. an' O. 'e 'ad, an' got the sack for
booze."

All hands had shaken down into their places,
and, despite the tyranny and hard driving, it was
good to be alive and afloat down there where the
trade winds blow. With the wind well on the
quarter and steady, the *Maid of Miramichi* was
tranquilly reeling off her 200 miles a day. Every
stitch of her snow-white canvas was set, even the
delicate little sky-sails, 180 feet above the deck,
were never furled for over a week on end. The
sky overhead was a brilliant blue, over which there
would occasionally pass a few light fleecy trade-
wind clouds ; the sea was a deeper blue, broken
only by the sparkling white crests of the wavelets,
the darting of flying-fish, or the leaping of a shoal
of albicore or bonita. The mild balmy wind droned
through the rigging, the sails cast deep cool shadows
over the spotless decks. Yes, it was good to be
alive, to be doing a sailorman's job aloft on spar or
rigging, and at night to sit on the main-hatch and
smoke and watch the mast-heads gently swaying
against the starry sky. A pleasant orderly life ;
even the hard-featured old man seemed to be
affected by it ; on one occasion, it was alleged,
he had been seen to smile ; and just as man may,
in time, get used to anything, so the men of the
port watch seemed to have settled down contentedly into their state of humble submissiveness.

As for those of the second mate's watch they had
become openly cheerful, and for the first time since
the commencement of the voyage snatches of song
were to be heard in the forecastle when it was their
second dog-watch below.

III.

There came a day, however, when the steady sailing breeze petered out, and if the captain had been seen to smile once during the favourable north-east trades, he certainly never did so in the belt of doldrums that followed them. During the whole of the next nine days the vessel made ninety miles, and that only by taking advantage of every light air that blew. For most of the time the surface of the sea was like a gently undulating sheet of glass ; then there would be a ruffle on the face of the water, a light air would spring up, and round would come the great yards, for night or day the highest air must find the sails trimmed ready to meet it. If they were not, and the captain happened to come on deck, the officer of the watch felt the lash of his bitter tongue, and promptly passed it on to the hands with interest. The light air might last for a few minutes, the sails would fill, the great vessel would slowly gather way, and by the time that the puff had died away again she might have sailed about half a mile. The sails would give a few flaps against the masts, then hang straight up and down without a flutter in them ; the sea would become glassy again. A little later the wind would come away from a different quarter, round would go the great yards again, and another half-mile would be gained. It was a weary task, this working through the doldrums. Occasionally, mostly at night, dark clouds would gather and lightning would play about overhead; the sky would present a weird appearance so threatening that they would lower away the sky-sail and royal yards and stand by the top-gallant halliards. But the wind never came; instead down would come the rain in enormous drops, flooding the decks and causing the surface of the sea to effervesce in miniature waterspouts.

During the daytime, when the sun had climbed for a couple of hours, there was a sickly smell of blistering paint, and the pitch oozed out from between the seams on deck. The officer of the watch brooded as he gazed moodily around the horizon searching for a breeze; the men slunk silently around the decks, going about their work, which had to be dropped, and the braces manned, on the slightest sign of a puff; everything had to be dropped for that. Tempers were frayed and nerves were on edge as the vessel drifted toward the Line. Then came a morning when the first real squall with wind in it struck them; it came hissing across the water preceded by heavy rain, and caused them to shorten sail in a hurry and amid some confusion. When the squall was over they discovered that they had picked up the south-east trades, and close-hauled on the port tack they stood away toward the south-west.

The south-east trades were succeeded in about

latitude 27° south by the westerlies ; the weather became colder, and it was no longer pleasant to knock about the deck bare-footed. A sudden ' pampero ' off the River Plate, which lasted two days, showed up some weak points in the standing and running rigging, but those were quickly remedied in readiness to face the greatest test of all—that of rounding the Horn ; and by the time that the vessel had arrived in the vicinity of that dreaded cape, both ship and crew were as fit for the ordeal as they could possibly be made. Soon they were battling into the teeth of a north-west gale, a battle that brought the best out of the officers of the ' blue-nose.' They drove their ship as relentlessly as they drove her crew. One day, staggering and plunging along with everything except the crossjack set, up to the main top-gallant sail, and leaning over at a fearful angle while everything aloft strained and cracked, they passed a large iron barque, head reaching under lower topsails.

The result of this cracking on was that when the officers did reluctantly give orders to take in a sail, it was only with the greatest difficulty that it could be secured. First, the men hauled from the deck on bunt-line and clew-line partially to subdue the slatting canvas. Then would come the order ' aloft and furl,' and the hands would crawl up the weather rigging and lay out on the jolting yard. Cotton canvas is a joy to look upon when glistening, snow white, in the sunlight, but it is hellish stuff to try and furl in a gale of wind off Cape Horn, when, wet and stiff and bellying out like a balloon,

it defies every effort of man to gather in its stub-
born folds. Swinging dizzily on the foot-rope suspended from the yard, and hanging on with one
hand to the slender iron jackstay which ran along
the top of it, they would fight the struggling thrashing monster, gradually master and subdue it, and
pass the gaskets round it to make it secure. Often
men would cry with pain and vexation as an extra
gust would tear the tough canvas from their
stiffened fingers just as they thought that they had
it fast. It was wild and dangerous work to tired
men, this swaying on a yard a hundred feet above
the deck, but there was one man on board who
enjoyed every moment of it, and that man was
W. Kuroki. He was in his element. Other men
pay large fees for the privilege of sitting at the feet
of university professors and acquiring knowledge
from them ; Kuroki was paying, by the endurance
of hardship, discomfort, and danger, for what he
deemed the privilege of sitting at the feet of those
marvellous ' blue-nose ' officers and learning from
them the highest arts of seamanship. Seldom did
they make a mistake. During the whole of that
Cape Horn passage they never lost a spar, a sail, or
even a rope-yarn, so sure was their instinct regarding the stresses and strains on masts, ropes,
and canvas. Yet they never shortened sail without
reason. When *they* took in a sail it was really time
that it was in, and that inveterate searcher after
knowledge, the little Japanese, watched their
every movement greedily. When a sail had to be
loosed or furled he was the first man into the rigging.
Imperturbable, cheery even during the dreariest

nights of depression—nights when the men of the watch below lay in their bunks, or sat on their sea-chests in the gloomy forecastle, waiting for the call of ' all hands shorten sail,' which they knew to be inevitable, while the vessel's bows crashed and pounded into the waves and the squalls shrieked outside,—W. Kuroki smiled his way around the Horn.

Hard driven, the *Maid of Miramichi* stood away to the south-west, desperately clinging on to any westing that she made, and when the wind eventually shifted to the southward she was in a position to weather the Horn on the other tack. Carrying every stitch of canvas which she could stagger under she stood away into the Pacific, then northward toward fine weather again. To William Jackson this Cape Horn passage, and the way that it had been accomplished, had been a revelation, and for one thing he was very thankful : during the time of their battling down there the officers had been more human, and they had not hazed the hands unnecessarily. It is true that the mate had always been ready to help with his heavy sea-boot the last man to get into the rigging when there was occasion to lay aloft and furl a sail, but, taking it all round, he had been less handy with his hands and feet than he had been in the fine weather. The food too, never very bad, for American and Nova Scotian vessels were usually well supplied in that respect, had been considerably better during the period of the bad weather.

This state of affairs did not, however, last ; within a week of their striking fine weather again

things were as bad as ever they had been ; even
the food was cut down to a minimum, so that the
men had barely strength to stand up to the strenuous work, much of it unnecessary, which they had
to do. To William Jackson the cruelties practised
at that time seemed to be calculated, as if they were
being carried out according to a plan. One day the
mate, after badly hammering one of the Scandinavians, pulled his victim on to his feet and ordered
him to fetch a bucket of water and a swab. He
then stood over the poor wretch and forced him to
mop up his own blood from the otherwise spotless
deck. That evening, in their second dog-watch
below, William Jackson found his friend the boatswain's mate sitting on the spare spar which was
lashed along the port bulwarks, and to that petty
officer he mentioned his suspicions. The boatswain's mate looked cautiously round before he
replied.

" You're quite right," he said in a low tone,
" an' I'll let you into the reason for it. When we
arrive in 'Frisco the season's crop o' wheat'll no'
be ready ; no, nor near ready. Likely enough the
ship'll go alongside o' Mission Wharf an' discharge
her coal, then she'll go across the Bay an' lie at
anchor off Saucilito or some such place, to wait for
a cargo. She'll be lyin' there for months, an' do
you suppose that the old man's going to keep the
hands by her all that time ? Not on your life. If
he can't run the present crowd out of her he'll
lose his reputation as a hard-case shipmaster an'
perhaps his job as well. Of course half o' the
crowd'll clear out the first night we're in harbour.

The boarding-house crimps'll be on board in full force, well armed with liquor, as soon as the anchor's down, for the whalers and sealers 'll be howlin' for crews, an' before the sails are properly fast you'll see chests and bags goin' over the side, and the old man'll no' stir hand nor foot to stop them. But there's the other half o' the men, like old Alphonse an' the squareheads, that no crimp'll ever catch; some o' them have wives an' children, an' they're no' goin' to make a present o' three months' pay to anybody. They're out to make the round voyage whatever happens, an' it's them that the old man and the big fella are tryin' to intimidate."

" Is desertion as easy as that out there ? " asked Jackson.

" Easy," echoed the boatswain's mate with a low laugh, " ay, it's easy enough, and sometimes it's desirable. Besides them that'll go with the crimps, some o' us'll no' stay. There's the Jap, for instance,—he wants to get back to Japan. Well, he can do it easier from 'Frisco than he can from the old country." He pitched his voice still lower. " Between ourselves," he continued, " I'm off, but mind you, no crimp'll get me. I've got friends there that'll get me a decent job either in 'Frisco or in one o' the canneries up the coast. What about you ? A well-educated man like yersel 'll find lots o' chances out there. You'll no be stoppin' by the ship ? "

William Jackson flushed slightly. Up till now he had not discussed his future with any one. He hesitated a moment before he spoke.

" No, I won't," he admitted.

" Well," said the boatswain's mate, " take my advice an' avoid the crimps like the plague, an' for God's sake don't touch liquor either aboard the ship or ashore until you're settled in a job an' have got your bearin's. You can never tell when it may be doped an' you'll wake up next mornin' outward-bound aboard a whaler." He put out his hand in the darkness and seized that of William Jackson. " Better still, mate," he continued, " you come with me an' I'll see you through."

The cold-blooded, calculated cruelty which had been practised all the way through the south-east trades was succeeded when they reached the belt of doldrums by a perfect orgy of persecution and brutality. The calms and light airs were even more prolonged and baffling than those which they had experienced in the Atlantic, and the captain, exasperated beyond measure at seeing his chance of a rapid passage dwindling away, took to drink. The mate joined him, and the pair of them seemed to think of nothing but persecuting the ' mules.' The second mate pursued the even tenor of his way. At times the mate cast longing eyes at some of the, to his idea, pampered sailors of the starboard watch, but the second mate clearly showed by his attitude that he would stand no interference, and the former had perforce to keep his hands and feet off the pampered ones. In the meantime, however, a feeling of desperation began to show itself amongst the men of his own watch, and they began openly to discuss chances of getting even with their persecutors. Bert Hawkins was the means of giving this feeling a temporary check. The Cockney had brooded over his fight with the mate on the day on which they left port, and believed that, had he not been so fuddled with drink that the finer points of pugilism had deserted him just when they were most required, he might have put up a better show. Now that the boot was on the other foot he determined to have another try. The fight, however, although more prolonged, could have no other result considering his adversary's height and weight. The mate, surprised at the Cockney's audacity, and slightly inebriated, got a little the worst of it at first, but when he came to himself he quickly sailed in and finished it. Again Bert Hawkins, after suffering fearful punishment, dropped on the deck and gasped—

" Orl right. I've 'ad enough."

This phrase of submission is usual at sea, and is always followed by a cessation of hostilities. To continue to hammer an opponent after that is equivalent to shooting men after they have surrendered. The mate, however, had no use for etiquette, and, moreover, he had no other preoccupation such as he had had on the previous occasion.

" Hev yew ? " he snarled. " I'll tell yew when yew've had enough."

Raising the Cockney from the deck he battered the unfortunate wretch into a state of insensibility ; then, throwing the inert body at the feet of the group of onlookers, he roared—

" Take that damned thing away, and if any of the rest of yew want to have a go, say so right naow." He paused. " Yes, any six of yew," he added contemptuously.

The terrible thrashing administered to Bert Hawkins only allayed the unrest for a couple of days, and the Cockney when he recovered was the most eager advocate of revolt. The men hung about in groups during their watch on deck at night, and brooded in their watch below in a fever of discontent which every fresh brutal act aggravated. Amongst other things they had noticed that the bruises inflicted by the mate during the hours of darkness were far worse than those made by his fists in daylight, and undoubtedly the reign of terror which he had established was a very real one. He wasn't idly boasting when he had said that he could take on any six of them—cowed and dispirited as they were. They had also noticed that the captain when on deck had a suspicious-looking bulge in the region of his hip-pocket. Sullen and desperate, and trying hard to screw up their courage, the men awaited their chance.

" I don't like the look o' things," the boatswain's mate remarked to William Jackson one hot calm evening. " Worms *will* turn, ay, even Squareheads and Dagoes."

IV.

The trouble came on the very day that they got clear of the doldrums when, having picked up the north-east trades, the vessel was heeling over to a spanking breeze. The captain, instead of being overjoyed at his good luck, was in a vile temper—the after-effects of brandy,—and during the last hour of the forenoon watch he had nagged the man at the wheel, old Alphonse—the best helmsman in the ship,—so much that the Belgian had answered him back—an unpardonable offence. At eight bells, when the starboard watch came on deck, the rumour went round that old Alphonse had not been allowed to leave the poop, and certainly he did not join his comrades in the forecastle for dinner. The captain and mate having taken their observations of the sun at noon, went below to work up the ship's position, and when they returned to the poop they noticed that the men of the port watch, having finished dinner, were clustered outside the forecastle waiting to see what was going to happen to their shipmate.

William Jackson was in the weather main rigging rattling down a portion of it ; below him, Kuroki was putting fresh seizings on one of the shrouds.

From his point of vantage Jackson could see all
that was happening on the poop, and occasionally
he paused in his work and glanced aft curiously.
He saw the captain and the mate stretch Alphonse's
arms above his head and then, with some marline,
they lashed his thumbs to the weather shrouds
in such a manner that, when the vessel was steady,
his feet just touched the deck ; when she rolled
ever so slightly, the whole weight of his body came
on his thumbs. It was a form of punishment which
had been practised years before in packet ships
and New Bedford whalers. The first time she
rolled the poor old man shrieked with the pain.
That was quite enough for William Jackson ; he
had stood by, not unmoved, when other men were
being struck and kicked ; he had felt that he had
no cause to interfere even when Hawkins was being
knocked insensible, for he had a very strict sense
of discipline, and he felt that the Cockney had, to
a certain extent, asked for it ; this, however, was
premeditated torture—a thing that no Englishman
could stand. Very deliberately he unslung the
marline-spike which he was using from round his
neck, hung the heavy, sharp steel tool on a shroud,
and descended the rigging. He walked aft and
mounted the lee-side of the poop, Kuroki at his
heels, crossed to the weather side which, in ships
of all nationalities, is sacred to the captain or
the officer of the watch, and drew his sheath-
knife.

" What in hell are *yew* doin' here ? " roared the
astonished mate, who was leaning against the rail
gloating over the struggles of Alphonse.

" I am going to cut that man down, sir," replied Jackson calmly.

" The hell yew are, yew mutinous swine," sneered the captain. " I've had my eye on *yew* for some time. Up he goes by the thumbs too, mister, and that bloody Jap alongside of him."

The mate withdrew his great fists from his trousers pockets ; on his right hand there gleamed something black—it was a knuckle-duster. His right arm swung back, but the blow never fell. William Jackson while in the navy had on one occasion, not so very long before, reached the final in the officers' heavyweight championship. Deftly slipping the mate, he cross-countered him, then drove right and left hard to the point. For a few seconds the giant tottered crazily on his feet, swinging his arms wildly, then he crashed heavily to the deck. Events now happened with bewildering rapidity ; there was a quick shout from Kuroki and the crack of a revolver shot, the bullet from which whizzed harmlessly to windward ; the revolver clattered to the deck, and the captain, white and sick, was leaning against the rail, his arm dangling helplessly by his side, rendered useless by a ju-jitsu trick of the Japanese. The men of the port watch who had been hanging about the forecastle door went rushing aft, and the poop-deck was quickly crowded.

Then followed tragedy, swift and deplorable, and deplored by no one more than the man who caused it. The young second mate had refused point-blank to have anything to do with the stringing up

of Alphonse. Sick at heart, he had busied himself
with some job amidships, and tried to keep his mind
from the evil deed which was being perpetrated on
the poop. He had, however, glanced along when
Jackson and Kuroki had gone aft, and had seen
what had happened afterwards. That was an entirely different matter. His superior officers had
been assaulted, and now the rush of the port watch
looked like mutiny. Snatching a heavy iron belaying-pin from the main fife-rail, he dashed up on
to the poop, the assembled men scattering before
him, and made straight for William Jackson, who
was about to cut Alphonse down. The poor old
Belgian had fainted. Kuroki was the only one in
the second mate's way. The little Japanese
dropped on one knee, and by another ju-jitsu trick
threw the rushing officer clean over his shoulder.
The latter brought up with terrific force, head first,
against a solid mooring bollard, and never moved
again. When they tried to pull him round they
found that he was dead : his neck had been dis-
located.

While Jackson was examining him and two of
the others were cutting Alphonse down, they were
startled by a great slatting of canvas aloft and a
rattling of blocks ; the vessel, which had been
leaning over to the fresh trade wind, had come on
an even keel. Jackson glanced at the wheel ; it
was deserted. The helmsman had left it to join the
others, and at the moment was kicking the pros-
trate mate on the head. The ship was flying up
in the wind, and in a few moments would be all

aback, with the prospect of damage to spars and
rigging.

"Hand to the wheel there and put the helm hard
up. Weather fore brace ; haul the foreyards round
and box her head off. *Look lively.*"

Subconsciously William Jackson had taken command.

V.

The first thing that William Jackson did after the vessel had been got under control and was again sailing with her sails full, was to put the captain and mate under lock and key, his main reason for this being to save them from the wrath of the crew. They were confined in the captain's cabin, a spacious room with a door aft, which led into his private bathroom, from which there was no other exit. The only door thus to be guarded was the one leading into the cabin from the saloon. This was locked, and an able-seaman armed with the captain's revolver, in which there were still five cartridges, was posted outside of it. Before placing the two officers in the cabin, Jackson had searched it for firearms. He found another revolver there, and also one in the mate's room. To avoid further trouble, he confiscated those by simply dropping them overboard.

It took some time to bring old Alphonse round, and then his spell of consciousness was a short one. He apologised for causing so much trouble, explained with one of his wistful smiles that he had a weak heart, and shortly afterwards expired. Just before sunset that evening the two victims of the

D

tragedy were buried. The tarpaulin had been taken off the main hatch, and one of the hatches placed on the lee-side of the deck in the way of an open gangway. The bodies of the second mate and Alphonse had been hurriedly sewn up in canvas by the sailmaker, with some heavy holy-stones at their feet to weigh them down, then placed upon the hatch with a flag covering them. There they lay, side by side, two aliens under the Red Ensign—the American cut off in the pride of his youth, the Belgian too old to be knocking about before the mast in a ' blue-nose.' William Jackson read the burial service from his Book of Common Prayer, while all hands, with the exception of the captain and mate, their sentry, and the helmsman, stood around bareheaded. The helmsman was Kuroki ; he had begged to be allowed to take the wheel.

" I am the Resurrection and the Life, saith the Lord." In solemn tones, disturbed only by the whispering of the trade wind in the rigging and the swish of the water along the sides, the ex-naval officer read the beautiful words of the service.

" For as much as it hath pleased Almighty God of His great mercy to take unto Himself the souls of our dear brothers here departed, we therefore commit their bodies to the deep."

At a sign from Jackson the boatswain's mate reverently and quietly pulled the flag aside, four of the men tilted up the hatch, and as the words, " who at His coming shall change our vile body, that it may be like His glorious body," escaped the solemn lips of the reader, the two corpses slid down

the hatch feet first and took the water simultaneously.

With William Jackson in command, Kuroki, who
was the only other member of the crew with a
knowledge of navigation, was put in charge of the
port watch, for they did not trust the boatswain,
and the boatswain's mate took command of the
starboard watch. The other petty officers ac-
quiesced in this arrangement; indeed the mutiny
and the tragedy which followed so closely upon it
had partially stunned every one on board. That
very night, however, there was trouble. Kuroki,
whose watch on deck it was, called Jackson and the
boatswain's mate about eleven o'clock and informed them that the steward had given the men
the key of the pantry in which the liquor was stored,
that almost every man in the watch was drunk,
and that they had tried to rush the captain's cabin
with the intention of murdering the two men who
were imprisoned there. That they had failed was
due to the staunchness of Bert Hawkins, who was
on guard and who had steadfastly refused all offers
of drink. Jackson called out the starboard watch
and spoke to the men gravely; the rioters were
subdued and expelled from the saloon, and an ugly
incident was closed. He then removed all liquor
from the pantry, placed it in the lazarette under
the saloon, and securely padlocked the hatch. The
next day he announced his intention to serve out a
tot of rum to all hands every evening, and there
was no further trouble in the way of liquor.

The days that followed were the most peaceful
that had been known on the *Maid of Miramichi*

since she had left Barry Dock. There were plenty
of stores on board, and a good supply of food was
issued ; the afternoon watch below was no longer
kept on deck, the ordinary watch and watch system
being introduced. For the first two days the men
loafed about discussing events ; after that, tired of
idleness they begged for work, and busied themselves with odd jobs about the deck. To the
thoughtless it was a welcome change from the hard
driving which had been their lot previously, but
Jackson, Kuroki, and the boatswain's mate had
many anxious discussions, for they realised the
necessity for restoring the vessel to her proper
officers as soon as they decently could. The two
former navigated the vessel just as ably as the
captain and mate could have done. She was close-
hauled on the starboard tack, making the best
course that she could through the north-east
trades, and was sailed throughout in a proper seamanlike manner. Below in the captain's cabin the
captain and mate sat in helpless suspense. By the
motion of the vessel, and the direction of the sun
as seen through the portholes, they could tell that
she was making the best course that she could
make in pursuance of her voyage, heading as near
to the wind as she would go consistent with pro-
gressing through the water, and making northing
but being edged off to the west, just as she would
have done had they been on deck themselves. They
weren't allowed to speak to any one ; the steward
served their meals in silence, and, indeed, with the
possible exception of the sycophantic boatswain, no
one wanted to have anything to do with them.

In the first dog-watch from four o'clock in the afternoon until six all hands would gather on the after-hatch and discuss matters, and it was at one of those gatherings that the nigger had a brain wave. He had during the past week been painfully spelling out a novelette which dealt with the doings of a doughty boy pirate, who a few centuries before had performed wild and wonderful deeds in the Spanish Main. He had pondered over this all day, and, still pondering, had taken his seat on the hatch. Then he suddenly addressed William Jackson.

"Cap'n," he said, "I jes' wanta know what we're steerin' north for?"

"W'y, ye goat," chipped in the ever-ready Hawkins, "we got t' steer north t' get t' 'Frisco, hain't we?"

"Cap'n," persisted the nigger, "what we wanta go to 'Frisco fur?"

"Simply because the ship happens to be bound there," Jackson replied with a smile. "Why, what's the idea? What's biting *you*?"

"Cap'n, fo' de lad's sake, turn 'er roun' right now an' run down to Callao. We kain't sell dis yar cargo o' coal in 'Frisco, 'cos it belongs to folks dere. But we *kin* sell it in Callao. Dey allus wantin' coal dere. Den," continued the nigger, warming to his subject, "we kin run down to Iquique an' load saltpetre dere, an' sell *dat* somewhere else. We's got de ship, we's got gen'elmen as can navigate 'er; what's de matter with turnin' pirates? Dere's heaps an' heaps o' dollars in it. Turn 'er roun', cap'n, doan' head for 'Frisco no mo'!"

It is always a sad task to dispel, with a strong

dose of practical common-sense, beautiful day-
dreams such as the nigger had conjured up, but
William Jackson saw that it must be done, for,
incredible as it may seem, some of the more ignorant
of the crew were becoming infected by the former's
enthusiasm. Very patiently Jackson explained
that the days of Spanish Main pirates were over,
and that if they shoved their noses into any port
in the civilised world with the ship, they would,
through the lack of a proper clearance and other
papers, find themselves in jail within twenty-four
hours. He went on further to explain that as it
was they all stood a pretty good chance of finding
themselves in jail as soon as the ship arrived in
San Francisco, for, no matter what the provocation
had been, they had been guilty of one of the gravest
of crimes—mutiny on the high seas.

"Golly !" exclaimed the nigger, his eyes rolling,
" den why we go to——"

" Oh, dry up, ya' black squall," exclaimed Hawkins impatiently. " Nah, 'ere's somefink practical.
We got ter go t' 'Frisco, hain't we ?   Orl right.
Wot's th' matter wiv doin' in them two blokes aft ?
I'll do the dirty work meself ; I got a grudge agin'
the big feller any'ow. Then fake the log-book t'
show as 'ow th' ole man, th' two mates, an' Alphonse was washed overboard. We all clears aht
an' gits off choki. Bill Jackson, Kuroki, an' the
bo'sun's mate kin stay by 'er an' claim salvige, an'
they deserves it. Well, wot abaht it ?   Anyfink th'
matter wiv it ? "

" There's nothin' the matter with it, Bert,
especially as you're quite willin' to do the butcher

work," replied the boatswain's mate, " only this. How many o' the hands'll be sober the night we arrive in 'Frisco ? "

" H'm ! " muttered the Cockney.

" Ay, h'm," continued the boatswain's mate, " damned few. An' what would be the result ? When the drink's in, the wit's out. The whole water front o' 'Frisco would be excited an' talkin' about a ship that had arrived without officers an' navigated by two A.B.s. There would be drinks galore. Besides the crimps, smart Yankee newspaper reporters would be all over us. Then somebody would blab, an' the first thing we would know we would be in jail with a charge of murder as well as mutiny against us. No, *that* cock'll no crow. Try again."

The croak of the nigger broke the solemn silence which followed.

" Cap'n," he pleaded earnestly, " doan' you go to 'Frisco."

VI.

By the time that they had reached the northern limit of the north-east trade wind the *Maid of Miramichi* had been forced well out into the North Pacific. It was succeeded by a westerly breeze, which enabled them to steer a straight course for their port ; and as William Jackson laid off that course on the chart, he realised with something of a shock that they had only a matter of about two thousand miles to go, and that with ordinary luck in the way of winds they should arrive within a fortnight. Clearly it was time that something was done, and he determined to interview the captain. He realised that he had a poor hand to play, and that bluff would have little chance of succeeding with those hard-featured men who were confined in the cabin. Still he could only try. Walking into the saloon one day after breakfast he ordered Bert Hawkins, who was on guard, to unlock the door of the temporary prison, and to keep handy with the revolver in case of trouble. It was the first time that he had seen either of the officers since the day of the mutiny, and they glanced up with an air of sullen indifference as he entered the cabin.

"Good-morning, gentlemen," he said affably. "I have just called to inquire about your health. There's no pressing hurry, of course, but I thought that after your—er—holiday you might be fit to take over the control of your ship again."

This opening remark was greeted by a perfect stream of profanity; the pent-up feelings of the past ten days overflowed and created a regular spate of it. Mr Hawkins, who was *persona grata* in such places as the Ratcliffe Highway and Tiger Bay in Cardiff—places where the art of forcible expression has by no means been neglected,—declared afterwards that he had never heard the equal of the combined efforts of the captain and the mate. The ex-naval officer did not, however, quail before this intense verbal attack; he leant coolly against the jamb of the open door, and calmly surveyed the inmates of the cabin. When they paused for breath he turned to Hawkins.

"These gentlemen seem to be rather peevish this morning," he remarked. "Perhaps I have called rather early." He made to step back into the saloon.

"What in hell do yew want, anyway," queried the captain.

"Oh, merely to know if you felt like doing your own job again. As I said before, there's no pressing hurry, but really I am getting rather bored with it."

"Yew carry on the way yew're doin'," replied the captain grimly. "When we get to 'Frisco yew'll get a spell. It'll be in jail, I guess, an' it'll be a pretty long one. One of yew'll be up fur murder, sure, an' the rest fur mutiny, an' yew bein' the ringleader 'll come off worst."

"Talking about murder, I suppose you know that you two murdered Alphonse," replied Jackson. "It seems to me that, in the eyes of the law, one crime is as bad as the other. In fact yours, having been done in cold blood, is probably the worse."

"The law!" the mate interjected. "What *yew* know about the law on the Pacific—" He stopped abruptly, checked by a scowl from his superior.

"Yep. Yew carry on to 'Frisco," the latter said with a sneer. "Yew'll know all about it there."

"You seem to be assuming that the ship is going to 'Frisco, captain," said Jackson.

For the first time the two officers showed sign of discomfiture. Jackson noticed it and took his cue from it.

"Where else kin yew take her without papers? Don't try that bluff on us—it don't go down here."

"Really, captain," replied Jackson, "you under-estimate my intelligence very badly. Let me explain. I have taken an inventory of the stores and I find that there are sufficient provisions on board to last us comfortably for about seven months. Now, just balance the possibilities. Do you imagine that we would take the ship into San Francisco and run our heads into a trap, when we have the whole world before us? Oh dear, no. You would hardly credit it, but the men are far more contented now than they were when you were in charge, and they wouldn't mind remaining at sea for a few more months—a regular yachting cruise it would be. I can sail right on past San Francisco up to Alaska ; I have even thought of Australia, or the southern part of New Zealand. There are lots of places off which we could scuttle the ship in deep water, get ashore in the boats, and then get away into the interior, where we would never be recognised. Of course, in that case, it would be necessary to leave you two on board, securely locked up, and let you sink with the ship. Very regrettable, of course, but as I said before, necessary."

" Yus," chimed in Hawkins, " an' we won't carry yer as far as that, neither. Jus' say the word, guvnor, an' blimey, the two of 'ems corpses within two minits."

" Friend Hawkins has thirsted for your blood for some time now," Jackson said in explanatory tones, " and I may mention that his desire is shared by the majority of the crew. You may remember the row they made the first night you were in here, until I got them stopped."

They did remember it. Neither of them was a coward, but they still recalled with a shudder that night when both of them felt groggy and the saloon seemed to be full of drunken fiends intent only on battering in the door of their prison and tearing them limb from limb. William Jackson had unintentionally played trump.

" Waal, what is yew're proposition ? " the captain asked, after a moment's silence.

" Ah, that's better," said Jackson cheerfully. " I rejoice to observe this spirit of sweet reasonableness. I will put it to you like this, captain— neither of us are particularly anxious that the authorities of San Francisco should know anything about the doings of the last ten days ; we, because we know perfectly well that, no matter what the provocation was, we have technically been guilty of mutiny—you because you have a murdered man to account for ; and besides," here the speaker played another trump, " no shipmaster would like it to be known that his ship had been taken out of his hands and navigated into port by two of the crew."

The captain nodded slowly. " Waal, go on," he said.

" All hands intend to clear out as soon as we arrive in port, and you know what that means— within forty-eight hours they will be scattered beyond recall. The log has not been written up since the day of the—er—incident, but I have kept a scrap log with the winds, courses, and all the necessary information that you require noted in it. What I propose is this. I will bring the log to you now and the mate can write it up, explaining the death of Alphonse and the second mate the best way he can. The official log is presumably in here. I would require that to be filled up too. I will give you until half-past twelve to do it ; then, if everything is correct, I will hand the ship over to you."

" Bring the log-book here an' we'll think it over," declared the captain.

William Jackson backed out of the cabin in much the same way as a lion-tamer backs out of a lion's cage, fetched the log-book from the mate's cabin and handed it, with his notes, to the captain. Then he left them and ordered Hawkins to relock the door. At noon he and Kuroki got the meridian

altitude of the sun, and worked up the ship's position as they had done every day since they had
taken charge. Jackson copied the latitude and
longitude upon a slip of paper and again sought
the captain's cabin. Its inmates seemed to him to
be almost suspiciously cheerful.

"Here's the log-book written up to date," the
captain said. "I guess that oughter satisfy yew."

Jackson took the log-book from him and turned
over its pages. On the date of the mutiny he found
that the mate had made an entry to the effect that
Alphonse had fallen overboard from aloft during a
squall, that the second mate had jumped overboard after him, and that neither of them had been
seen again. From that date onward the log was a
copy of the notes which he, himself, had written.

"Capital," he said cheerfully. "You are a pair
of first-class liars, if I may say so. I couldn't have
done it better myself. You are free now to take
charge whenever you like, sir, but remember—no
brutality."

"I guess yew kin hand over that gun," said
the captain to the able-seaman who had relieved
Hawkins.

"Oh, no," replied William Jackson swiftly.
"I'll take care of *that*, sir, and I warn you now that
if there is any breach of our contract, I shan't
hesitate to use it."

VII.

Neither William Jackson, Kuroki, nor the boatswain's mate were at all delighted with the bargain which the former had made with the captain, but they realised that it was possibly the best that could have been made under the circumstances. Far better, they argued, that the ship should go into San Francisco under her own officers than it would be to adopt any of the other schemes that had been suggested. In the first case, if the story of the mutiny reached the authorities—and they built their hopes that it would not on the fact that the officers would then have Alphonse's death to explain away—well, they would just have to take their punishment; but in the second case they would be criminals, slinking about the world obsessed by the dread of discovery. For a couple of days all went well : the captain and mate were fairly subdued. Then it was noticed that the latter was having many long talks with the boatswain, and that that petty officer was making friends with one or two of the men of the port watch who had been lukewarm throughout. One afternoon the boatswain leered at Bert Hawkins in such a cunning and suggestive manner that the redoubtable Cock-

ney would, in his own words, have " dotted 'im
one," had he not been warned by the others against
doing anything of the sort. That night the mate
began to get abusive again, and at four o'clock in
the morning one of the men of the starboard watch,
who had just been relieved from the wheel at the
change of the watch, entered the forecastle with
blood streaming from his mouth. The mate had
hit him because he had not been sufficiently quick
in passing the helm orders.

Here was a distinct breach of the contract, and
before turning in, the boatswain's mate, Jackson,
and Kuroki discussed the matter anxiously in low
tones, so that their shipmates in the forecastle
might not be disturbed, for their hours of sleep
were few. They could come to no decision, so turned
in. Jackson tossed uneasily in his bunk thinking
matters out. He had meant every word of his
threat to the captain, and decided that he would
interview that individual as soon after breakfast
as possible. He dozed off, but about seven o'clock
was wakened, and found Kuroki and Hawkins
standing by the side of his bunk.

" Turn aht, Bill," said the Cockney ; " them
bastards aft there 'ave done the dirty on us."

Jackson quickly scrambled out of his bunk, and
his first action was to reach for the revolver which
he had placed under his pillow.

" It's no good, old chap," said Kuroki ; " I've
stowed it away. There's a British man-of-war
alongside."

William Jackson went out of the dark forecastle
on to the newly scrubbed deck, and blinked into

the slanting rays of the morning sun. The *Maid of Miramichi* was forging very slowly through the water, her main-yards aback to partially check her progress, and signals of distress were flying from her peak. About a cable's length to windward and slightly ahead, a steamer flying the White Ensign was coming to rest under a reversed propeller, and a boat, fully manned, was being lowered down her side. It took the water, cast off smartly, and was rowed across the intervening stretch of sea. It crossed the Nova Scotia vessel's bows, and lay-to with tossed oars waiting for her to come up. A boat-rope was thrown into it, and it was soon fast alongside. The men of the watch on deck, most of whom had been standing by the boat-rope, and those of the watch below, who had turned out to a man, gazed with interest at the boat's crew—the first strangers they had seen for well over four months. A young sub-lieutenant, clad in blue jacket and white trousers, and wearing a cap with a white cover, came briskly up the side-ladder which had been put over, followed by four armed seamen. Two others remained in the boat.

The sub-lieutenant made his way aft to the poop, where the captain explained why he had hoisted the distress signals ; he had had a mutiny on board, he said, and he feared another.

" Do you want an armed guard placed on board ? " the sub-lieutenant asked.

" No, I guess we kin do without that," the captain replied, " but I would like yew to take the ringleader aboard of yewre gunboat."

" I shall have to get permission to do that."

"Waal," said the captain, "that ship o' yewres is within hail. Yew kin ask it."

"Thanks, but I have no intention of straining my vocal chords, or whatever it is that one hails with. Here, Smith, got your flags ? Right ! Semaphore across : 'Mutiny on board. Master wishes ringleader removed. Have I your permission to take him on board *Persimmon ?* '"

One of the naval ratings saluted, and commenced to semaphore to the man-of-war, which by this time had backed astern and then come up on the merchantman's lee-quarter.

"Do yew see that yellow Jap along there ? " said the captain. " I've but a little charge of murder against him."

"Indeed," the sub-lieutenant remarked politely. " Is that the man you wish me to remove ? "

"Guess not. Yew take that big Britisher ; I'll fix the rest of them."

Smith again saluted. " Message from the ship, sir," he said. " Captain says, ' Yes, and hurry up about it.' "

"Fetch your man along," said the sub-lieutenant.

"Jackson," the mate bellowed, " lay along aft here."

William Jackson proceeded aft, and stood below the break of the poop facing the little group. The sub-lieutenant addressed him—

"The captain reports that you drew a knife on him and that you were the ringleader in a mutiny. Have you anything to say before I remove you to that sloop-of-war ? "

Jackson drew his blunted sheath-knife and exhibited it.

" That is the knife, sir," he said. " It wasn't drawn on the captain, but for another purpose. As for the mutiny—I admit my share in it, but there were extenuating circumstances both before and afterwards."

" You can explain that in a court of law," replied the sub-lieutenant. " Get your kit and get into the boat."

" Better put him in irons, mister," suggested the mate ; " I'll fetch 'em up."

" When I want your advice on how to carry on my job, I'll ask for it," replied the young naval officer curtly. " Smith, see that this man gets his kit and gets into the boat."

" He's got a revolver o' mine, mister, an' I want it," said the captain.

" Smith, see that he doesn't stow away a revolver with his kit."

" Ay, ay, sir," replied Smith.

William Jackson went forward to the forecastle accompanied by Smith, while the rest of the naval party proceeded along the deck to where the side-ladder dangled from the top-gallant rail, with the boat lying at the foot of it. Presently Jackson appeared, accompanied by the boatswain's mate and Kuroki, the latter carrying Jackson's canvas bag. Smith brought up the rear.

" No revolver in the kit-bag or on the prisoner's person, sir," he reported.

" Hell, I want that revolver," roared the captain.

" Well, I am afraid that you will have to look for

it yourself," replied the sub-lieutenant. "Get into the boat, you men."

The crew of the *Maid of Miramichi* stood sullenly by, only the boatswain's mate, Hawkins, and Kuroki daring to bid Jackson farewell.

"Good-bye, Bill," said the little Japanese, as he wrung Jackson's hand. "Keep up the pecker."

The boat pushed off and made for the sloop, which was now lying astern. As it passed along aft Jackson looked up at the sailing ship's poop, which the captain and mate had just regained. Both of them regarded him with malevolent stares, in fact that of the captain was almost demoniac in its intensity. The mate shook his fist in the direction of where the men were clustered forward, and as he did so the young sub-lieutenant glanced upward and caught both the menacing gesture and the malevolent looks. He shuddered slightly and turned a more kindly eye on Jackson, who sat in the bow of the boat, his bag by his side. The latter was clad in a faded blue dungaree suit and was barefooted; on his head was a battered soft felt hat. His face was impassive, but his thoughts were running riot. So this was the way he was returning to the navy. He hoped that no one on the sloop would recognise him. Unfortunately there had been heavy rain the night before and he had caught enough rain-water in a bucket to have a bath, and afterwards had shaved five days' growth from his face. His eye caught the White Ensign floating lazily from the peak, and he realised that he would probably give himself away by uncon-sciously saluting the quarter-deck when he was

eventually ordered on to it. To remove the temptation to do so he took off his hat and thrust it under
the lashing which was round his bag. At last they
reached the deck of the sloop, where they were
received by the first lieutenant.

" Turn your prisoner over to the master-at-
arms," the latter said. " The captain is having
breakfast, but he'll see him later."

" Wot'll I do with the prisoner, sir ? " asked the
master-at-arms ; " put 'im in the cells ? "

" Certainly not," replied the sub-lieutenant indignantly. " Take him forward and see that he
gets some food."

As William Jackson passed along the deck of the
sloop the musical cries of the crew of the *Maid of
Miramichi* floated across the intervening water ;
her hands were bracing up the main-yards and
sheeting home the courses. Her snow-white sails
bellied out gracefully as they filled ; the low black
hull careened over slightly and commenced to sheer
through the water. She seemed to be lifelike in
her beauty—one of the most graceful of man's
creations. Yet man's inhumanity had caused her
to carry a load of human strife and suffering.

VIII.

Commander the Hon. Charles Clinton-Browne, who commanded Her Britannic Majesty's sloop-of-war *Persimmon*, was a strict disciplinarian. In appearance he was of medium height, well set up, with clean-shaven face and blue eyes ; one could almost describe him as a typical naval officer. He dressed immaculately and affected an eye-glass—his friends declared that it was more ornamental than useful,—which he wore suspended at the end of a piece of black ribbon, called by the irreverent sub-lieutenant a lanyard. In moments of severity —when he was dealing with a certain class of defaulter—he screwed it into his left eye, and, with an effort, held it there. It was shipped in position when, about half-past ten that morning, William Jackson was brought into his roomy comfortable cabin by the master-at-arms, and through it he regarded the barefooted, shabbily-dressed mutineer from the *Maid of Miramichi* as if the latter were a thing unclean. Before him, on the table at which he sat, was a sheet of foolscap on which he evidently intended to make notes.

" H'm," he commenced curtly. " Name and nationality ? "

"William Jackson, sir. British."

The reply of the speaker affected the Hon. Charles Clinton-Browne in an extraordinary manner. The eyeglass shot out of its position and brought up at the end of its lanyard, while he gazed in astonishment at the able-seaman who stood before him. Quickly recovering himself he readjusted the eyeglass, asked one or two further questions in an abrupt manner, and then addressed the master-at-arms.

"I wish to speak to this man alone," he said. "Take up a position at the end of the alley-way and see that we are not disturbed."

"Ay, ay, sir," replied the imperturbable master-at-arms, and left the cabin, closing the door behind him. The commander opened a box of Turkish cigarettes and pushed it toward William Jackson.

"Sit down, Cartaret, and have a cigarette," he said. "I haven't seen you since that time that I dined with you in the flagship's wardroom at Malta, but when you spoke I remembered your voice. You were one of the fellows that I really looked up to when we were on the *Britannia*, and I can't make out how the devil you got into your present predicament. There surely must be more in it than meets the eye. Come on, man to man and heart to heart, let's have the whole damned story."

It took 'William Jackson' or, as we should now call him, Cartaret, nearly half an hour to tell the story, and the commander listened to it intently. When it was finished he said—

"Cartaret, there's no necessity for me to assure

you that I believe every word you have said. Would you mind standing up again for a little ? " He opened the cabin door. " Master-at-arms," he shouted, " tell my servant to bring me a whisky-and-soda from the wardroom."

The servant appeared with the drink, placed it on the table, and left the cabin, again closing the door.

" Right ! " said the commander. " Now sit down and lap that up and have a cigarette, while I do some thinking. My mind works somewhat slowly—I never was a brainy devil like you."

After about five minutes of intense thought the Hon. Charles Clinton-Browne delivered his verdict.

" Cartaret," he said, " you are in the very devil of a hole. Upon my word I don't blame you for what you did ; I would have done the same myself —if I had had the pluck, but the trouble is that you will have to face a court of law in San Francisco. We are bound to Vancouver, where I would be obliged to land you, and you would promptly be extradited. You probably don't know anything about justice as it is ladled out at present on the Pacific Slope. There is at least one judge in San Francisco who would give you six months' hard labour for being a British seaman to begin with, and then try you afterwards. An American citizen has been killed and two others assaulted, for if the mate isn't one already he will be before the trial comes off. Mutiny on the high seas is a grave enough offence at any time, but under those circumstances they will certainly hang the Jap—for Japs aren't popular either—and give you a rather long term of penal servitude. As to the murder of the Belgian—that will never be proved against them. Witnesses hostile to them will be shanghaied out of the way, and they will manage to get some of the crew to give evidence for them. Believe me, there will be lots of dirty work and some lovely lying.

"I am afraid that I won't be able to see you again, but I'll tell the first lieutenant to look after you—he is a really good chap. You may also expect a few visits from the navigator; he also is one of the best—one of the Hungry Hundred. Good-bye, old man, and the best of luck to you."

He shook Cartaret warmly by the hand, and then opened the door.

"Master - at - arms," he shouted, "take the prisoner forward; then give my compliments to the first lieutenant, and tell him that I wish to see him."

That afternoon the Hon. Charles Clinton-Browne, the first lieutenant, and the navigator sat in the former's cabin poring over a large scale chart of the coast-line below Vancouver, and talking very earnestly. Eventually they came to some decision, and the two latter rose to go.

"How did he come to leave the service, sir?" the first lieutenant asked before he and the navigator left the cabin.

"Hanged if I know," replied Clinton-Browne. "It had nothing to do with his job, for he was a topping officer, and every one thought that he would go far. He was dashed popular too. There was the usual crop of rumours, the most generally accepted being that it was another case of *cherchez la* damned *femme*."

IX.

About ten o'clock one night, a few days later, the *Persimmon* was steaming along a high rocky coast which was indented at intervals by small bays. It was pitch dark, with a slight drizzle ; there was no wind, and the sea was smooth except for a gentle swell ; the moon was due to rise about midnight. The junior watch-keeper—the sub-lieutenant—was on the bridge, while the navigator, he of the Hungry Hundred, leant over the table in the chartroom ostensibly working out some abstruse problem in algebra on a large sheet of paper. Every now and then he would step outside and survey the coast-line ahead through his binoculars. To him there presently came the sub-lieutenant.

" Pilot," said the latter, " excuse me for inter-rupting this fascinating game of chasing the wily x, but it seems to me that the course you have set is rather fine. That cape ahead is fairly close, and only a little on the starboard bow."

" Right-o, Cecil ! " replied the navigator. " It's steep-to, and I am watching it. I am working out a very interesting problem."

He added an xyz^2 to the mass of figures on the paper, and gazed on his handiwork with satisfaction.

The sub-lieutenant gave him a pitying look, and returned to the bridge. As the high rocky headland to which he had referred drew abeam, it seemed to him to be much too close, for the noise which the slight swell made as it rolled up the rocks could be heard quite distinctly : a four-point bearing gave the distance off, when abeam, as two cables. Just round the corner from the cape was a little bay, and as it passed astern it opened out some scattered lights, showing that in the bight of the bay there was a small village. About a mile and a half ahead, in fact extending a little on the other bow, was another high headland—it marked the other horn of the bay—toward which the *Persimmon* was fast steaming. The sub-lieutenant again sought the navigator, and found him, binoculars in hand, with one foot outside the chartroom door.

" Pilot," said the sub-lieutenant, " when I was in England last I dropped into a place of amusement erroneously described as a music hall, and there I heard a red-nosed comedian singing a song entitled ' What ho, she bumps ! ' If *you* don't come on the bridge and do something, I also shall be singing it —very soon—the subject of it being this valuable sloop-of-war."

" Cecil," replied the navigator earnestly, " sooner than listen to you singing I would do anything. Lead on."

From the bridge the navigator, through his glasses, studied the bay and the point on the other side of it toward which the *Persimmon* was heading.

" Excellent ! Very good experiment," he exclaimed loudly. Then to the telegraph-man, " Stop the engines—full speed astern."

Under the influence of her reversed propeller the sloop soon lost her speed, but while she was doing so she was swinging to starboard as single-screw ships with right-handed propellers usually do when their engines are going astern, so that before she had lost all headway she had proceeded some little distance into the bay.

" Excellent, very good experiment," repeated the navigator to the sub-lieutenant, but loud enough for the telegraph-man, the quartermaster, and any one else around to hear. " Do you see that cape we just passed ? "

" Just missed, you mean," said the rather bewildered junior in a low voice.

" All right, you owl," was the reply in a similar tone ; then louder, " It is stated that that cape contains some mineral which exerts a strong magnetic influence on ship's compasses. I have just proved that statement to be wrong. I set a course to pass two cables off it, and, behold, she did so : the compass wasn't deflected one degree. Excellent ! "

The *Persimmon* had now gathered sternway, and was backing out toward the open sea. Now if a man is so unfortunate as to fall overboard from a single-screw steamer, especially if she is light, unless the helm is instantly put hard over to cant her head toward the side on which he fell, and even then unless she is very lively on it, he is almost certain to be sucked into the propeller and cut to pieces ; it is almost impossible to get it stopped in time. It

is really safer to fall overboard when the vessel has
sternway, for in that case you go round the bow,
and there is no whirling atrocity at that end to cut
you up. It is significant, therefore, that just as the
Persimmon began to gather sternway, a figure clad
amongst other things in a life-belt slid down a rope
just on the after-side of the bridge on the port side
—all hands who happened to be on deck being on
the other side gazing at the rocks—and, paddling
noiselessly, floated away forward and disappeared
into the darkness ahead. The rope's end down
which he had slid was quickly hauled on board
again. The sloop being now well clear of the bay,
her engines were put ahead; the navigator, re-
marking that he had made enough experiments for
one night, laid off a safe course, and announced his
intention of going to sleep. The sub-lieutenant
yawned and longed for eight bells and the end of
his watch, so that he might do the same, for he
realised that there would be no more excitement
that night.

The next morning there was a hue and cry, and a
search for the prisoner, but he was not to be found.
The wardroom was sympathetic. " Poor devil,"
some one said, " he knew that he was in for a long
spell of jail and sooner than face it he went overboard." The lower-deck was also sympathetic, in
the main—even although that moulder of public
opinion, the gunner's mate, had declared that
' mutiny *was* mutiny,'—for the members of the
boarding party had formed a very poor opinion of
the master and mate of the *Maid of Miramichi*, and
Smith, during his short sojourn in her forecastle,

had picked up quite a lot of information and had spread it freely amongst his shipmates. That same evening the *Persimmon* arrived in Vancouver, where her commander reported the matter to the proper authorities. She only remained there one day, then sailed for Esquimalt, and the receipt of a large home mail at the latter place had the effect of dismissing the mutineer and his fate from the minds of the great majority of her crew. They did not stay long in that pleasant little harbour, but proceeded up the coast to do some surveying.

Shortly afterwards anxiety began to be felt in shipping circles in San Francisco and along the water front for the *Maid of Miramichi*. She was now 165 days out from Barry Dock, not an excessively long passage certainly, for a British four-master had arrived a week before, over 200 days out from the United Kingdom ; but that vessel, after battling to make westing round Cape Horn for nearly two months had given up the struggle, squared away, and ran before the wind right round the world *viâ* the Cape of Good Hope and New Zealand. There was, moreover, no comparison between her case and that of the *Maid*, nor had the latter vessel foundered off the Horn, for Lloyd's agent at Vancouver reported that she had been spoken when 140 days out by H.M.S. *Persimmon* in Lat. 32°-10′ N., Long. 144°-12′ W. She was then only about 1500 miles from her port of destination, and, as the San Francisco newspapers took care to point out, with the strong westerly winds which prevailed at that time, she could easily have made the distance in seven days.

Weeks passed by ; she was placed on the overdue list, then finally posted at Lloyd's as missing. The San Francisco ' Examiner ' referred, in an article with glaring headlines, to her loss as another unfathomable mystery of the ocean ; they even compared it with the famous case of the *Marie Celeste*. To the officers of the *Persimmon*, away up by Queen Charlotte's Island, the mystery did not, however, appear to be quite so unfathomable. The sub-lieutenant recalled the scowl of the captain, the menacing gesture of the mate, and the missing revolver, and surmised that there had been further trouble on board ; while the commander, first lieutenant, and navigator, who had further inside knowledge, probably came very near to the truth. They believed that the crew, goaded beyond endurance, and encouraged by their easy success on the previous occasion, had again mutinied ; that this time there had been no strong hand of William Jackson to steady them and keep them from liquor, with the result that, with most of the hands drunk, the vessel had been allowed to come up into the strong wind before which she was running, had broached to, and foundered.

But, whatever was her fate, the *Maid of Miramichi* was never heard of again, nor was a single trace of her ever found. None of those articles which bear a vessel's name, such as wash-deck buckets, life-buoys, branded oars, or name-pieces of boats, ever came to light to give a clue to the tract of water in which she was lost ; nor did any one of her crew ever come back to reveal the manner in which the tall ship had been overwhelmed, or describe the anguish of the last grim struggle against death.

X.

Some twenty years afterwards the Hon. Charles Clinton-Browne, now a rear-admiral, found himself upon the Australian station. In appearance he had altered very little. He was still immaculately dressed—one might still describe him as a typical naval officer—and he still affected an eye-glass, which by this time, however, was more useful than ornamental.

Shortly after his arrival on the station, Melbourne Cup day came round, and the admiral motored out to Flemington as the guest of one of Melbourne's most prominent citizens. This citizen's party was a large and merry one ; the weather was delightful, the lovely gardens were a blaze of flowers, and the enclosures were thronged with beautifully dressed women. By the afternoon brightness and gaiety reigned everywhere save only in the hearts of the punters, and in those there was nothing but unrelieved gloom. Their troubles had started early in the day—with the very first race, in fact—and had continued without a break. Favourite after favourite had gone down. The horse which should in the opinion of the news-papers, the experts, and the tipsters have won the

E

Cup, not only failed to connect with that trophy, but didn't finish in the first half-dozen.

" What the hell I'll say to the missus to-night," one punter remarked in the admiral's hearing, " let alone what I'll say to the butcher and grocer next Monday, the Lord only knows."

The party to which the admiral was attached had fared no better than the majority of the punters ; in fact most of them had plunged rather heavily on the favourite for the Cup. Included in the party was a number of young ladies who spoke of their losses with the humorous fortitude usually displayed on those occasions, although some of them, the admiral shrewdly suspected, had lost more than they could afford. Just before the last race most of the admiral's friends were clustered in a group in the paddock, consulting their race-cards rather hopelessly, and wondering how they could partially recoup their losses, when a tall, well-groomed, clean-shaven man approached them. The admiral's host recognised him.

" Hullo ! " he exclaimed, " here's a man who has a horse running in this race, so he ought to know something. He is one of the newest members of our squattocracy : just acquired Walaroi, a large station out Bachus Marsh way ; dead straight too. Here, Walaroi, I want to introduce you to the admiral."

The two men bowed. The squatter seemed to be well known to the other members of the party, and after a little chaff he took the admiral to one side.

" Had a good day, admiral ? " he asked.

" Not so bad, but my bets are very modest.

Strange to say, I picked the winner of the Cup and backed it against every one's advice, but I was only betting in shillings while the other people were playing about with pounds, and *they* were all on the favourite. I am afraid that the whole party is pretty well down the drain."

" H'm, too bad," said the squatter.

" They tell me that you have a horse running in this race. If you could manage to give me a decent tip I would like to pass it on to the others—some of those girls could do with it, I know."

The squatter regarded his companion rather whimsically.

" Look down your race-card, admiral," he said, " and if there is anything there that reminds you of an incident that happened about twenty years ago, back it. It's the best thing of the day."

The admiral frowned slightly, screwed his eye-glass well into his eye, and turned over the card. The squatter watched him intently, his eyes twinkling with a whimsical humour. He imagined that he could divine the admiral's thoughts. Confound the fellow, the latter would be thinking, why the devil couldn't he tell me the name of the horse right off instead of indulging in parables? Still frowning, the admiral sought the page which contained the runners for the last race, and half-way down it he found this entry—

7. *Mr L. Cartaret's br. f. Maid of Miramichi.* 3 *yrs.* 8 *st.* 2 *lb.* . . .

For the second time in the course of this narrative the Hon. Charles Clinton-Browne's eye-glass shot out of its position and brought up with a jerk at the end of its lanyard. Again he quickly adjusted it, and stared with astonishment at the man in front of him.

"Well, I'm damned!" he exclaimed loudly.

"So shall I be, admiral, financially anyway, unless I can do something over this last race. Only this morning I stood in the paddock beside the Cup favourite and was assured by the greatest racing expert in Australia that it couldn't lose. And a fat lot the glue-footed brute cared about *that* opinion when it struggled in seventh. So, Mr Cartaret, please, if you can't put us on to something good, we will all have to go out charring."

The speaker was one of the youngest and fairest members of the party. Mr Cartaret advised her to back his filly and to tell her friends to do the same; indeed so confident was he, that he suggested that they could safely put their shirts, or the equivalent, on it. Then he dashed off to see his jockey before the horses went out, while the others got busy putting their money on.

His confidence was not misplaced. Maid of Miramichi romped home at the satisfying odds of 8 to 1, and it was a very cheery party indeed, its gaiety entirely restored, which left the course and motored back to Melbourne. That night the admiral had to attend an official dinner-party, but he got away from it fairly early, and he and Cartaret sat in the latter's rooms far into the night.

"Now don't forget that you are dining with me on board the flagship on Friday," the admiral said as they parted.

"I'm not likely to forget it," replied Cartaret.

" I haven't been on board of a service vessel since that night I left the old *Persimmon* so unostentatiously."

" William Jackson," said the admiral with mock severity, for under the influence of Cartaret's hospitality he was feeling nicely mellow, " I know nothing about how you left the *Persimmon*."

" Perhaps not," replied Cartaret, with a chuckle, " but your number one did."

" You'll meet *him* on Friday," said the admiral, " his ship arrives to-morrow."

TWO TYPHOONS.

I.

THE menace of an approaching typhoon brooded over Hong Kong Harbour. Since daybreak the weather had been sultry and oppressive; now, about noon, squalls which brought with them a fine drizzling rain were sweeping at intervals across the water, blotting out the shipping. For hours the Peak, with its many white European residences, which usually show up so distinctly against its green background, had been completely obscured. Up at the observatory the first warning storm signal had been hoisted by the authorities; but, owing to the squalls, that, or any subsequent ones which might replace it, could only occasionally be seen by the anxious watchers on board the ships.

The large cargo steamer *Dulnain*, which was due to sail at noon for Java, was lying in the harbour with derricks down, all ready for sea. She had finished discharging her cargo about three hours before, and was in ballast trim; already one of the two anchors with which she had been moored had been hove up and secured. Her captain, however, was in a quandary. From the reading of his own barometer, from the warning signal, and, in addition,

from information supplied to him by the harbour
authorities when he had been ashore about an hour
before, he was aware that somewhere between the
Bashee Islands far to the east, where it had been
bred, and Hong Kong there was proceeding in a
westerly direction an intense revolving storm. He
knew that this colossal disturbance, covering many
hundreds of square miles, was coming on like a
gigantic cart-wheel at the rate of about two hundred miles a day, and that quite possibly the wind,
which was rotating round its centre, would be at-
taining a strength of at least a hundred miles an
hour. Clearly it was a thing to be avoided, but the
point was that the centre of it was not due in the
vicinity of the China coast for a matter of thirty-
six hours, and the latest information which he had
received was that it would probably strike in somewhere to the north. Now he was bound to the
south, and if he got away at once he would save at
least a couple of days' delay, and possibly run into
fine weather within twelve hours. The real crux
of the matter was whether the storm *would* actually
strike in to the north, or whether it would come
straight on, or, worst of all, even go farther south.
As he stood in the chart-room on the bridge consulting with his chief officer, he earnestly wished
that he had some further information.

" Look here, Simpson," he said to the officer,
" the harbour-master expected another cable from
the observatory in the Philippines about noon.
The ship's sampan is still alongside ; slip ashore
just as you are in your oilskin coat and rubber boots,
run up to the harbour office, and, with this wind,

you can be back with any message they have in less than half an hour."

"Very good, sir," replied the chief, and proceeded along the deck to the gangway ladder, at the foot of which, as the captain had said, the sampan was still lying. This craft was owned and commanded by a lady—one of a very numerous tribe which attends to the deep-sea shipping in Hong Kong Harbour, half of whose members answer to the name of Sampan Mary,—and it was her permanent home, as the cooking-pots and other domestic utensils which usually lumbered its deck showed. She was dressed in tunic and trousers made of a black silk-like material, and wore a huge mushroom-shaped hat, and as the chief officer descended the gangway ladder she was busy with her crew, which was composed of her sons and daughters of various ages, putting a close reef in the sampan's main-sail. The deck had already been cleared of everything movable.

"I want you to take me ashore, Mary," said the chief officer. "I am only going up to the harbour-master's office, and will come straight back."

"No bloody fear," replied Mary civilly, but not ceasing work for a moment. "Typhoon come—me go."

"Where are you going to?" asked the chief.

"Other side," replied Mary, waving her hand in the direction of the Kowloon shore. "Look see, all sampan go other side."

The reefing operation being completed, Mary took the helm, and the youthful crew, under her direction, hoisted the sail. One of them pushed the bow off with a boat-hook, the sail filled on the port tack, and with a cheerful wave of her dirty paw Mary disappeared into the mist of another squall. The chief officer gazed about to see if there was any other means of getting ashore, but any sampan which passed within hail took no notice ; as Mary had said, they were all going to the other side. He returned to the bridge, and reported his failure to the captain.

"I was rather afraid of that," said the latter. "Ever since that big typhoon a few years ago when, through some misunderstanding, unknown thousands of them were drowned, they have been jumpy and nervous. Before that they would hang on until the last minute ; now as soon as the warning signal is hoisted they begin to panic to get away across to the other side. There is a large shallow bay over there where they pack themselves in and lie in absolute safety. All the same, it is high time that *we* did something. The centre of this typhoon may not be due for some time, but there will be some devilish weather before very long. What to do ? That's the problem."

The captain's mind was very undecided, and indecision was a thing which he loathed. A crisis which called for immediate action never found him wanting : the correct order seemed to spring to his lips instantaneously. The solving of this problem, which he had ample time to think over, was a different matter. Two opposing courses lay open to him—either to seek shelter in one of the numerous anchorages around Hong Kong and remain there in safety until the storm had passed, or to proceed boldly to sea and steam as fast as his ship could go to the south, hoping to get clear before the worst of the storm would reach him. In his indecision he almost wished that he could lay his reason for those two courses before a competent authority, and abide by what that authority decided. This was, of course, impossible, but just then a solution which had something in it of that nature presented itself.

"The Apcar boat is heaving up, sir," said the chief officer.

"Is she?" replied the captain apathetically. A moment later he spoke with some animation. "By Jove, she is bound to Singapore—to the south the same as we are. Her captain is an old hand on the coast; he has been in this trade for twenty-five years, and besides he has been lying closer inshore and may have got later information. In any case we can't stay here. Heave aweigh, Simpson. If he goes to sea we will follow him; if not, we will run in for shelter behind Stone-cutters."

Before the Apcar boat could be got under way another, and fiercer, squall came howling up the harbour, completely blotting her out from view, but presently a deep-throated bellow from her steam whistle, farther east, seemed to indicate that she was bound to sea. The captain of the *Dulnain*, as soon as his anchor was aweigh, cautiously proceeded to follow. As he felt his way slowly toward the Ly-mun, the narrow channel which is the eastern entrance to Hong Kong, he became aware that the surface of the water in his vicinity was alive with moving craft. Ghostly shapes of junks and sampans would loom through the rain, all on the port tack, running as hard as they could for shelter ; while the whistles and syrens of deep-sea steamers showed that they also were under way and making for Kowloon, the back of Stone-cutters Island, or one of the small bays farther to the west. Evidently he had not made his move a moment too soon.

The weather became clearer, and by the time that the *Dulnain* was entering the Ly-mun the rain had ceased, although another black squall could be seen working up from the south-west. About a mile ahead was the Apcar boat taking advantage of the clear spell, and steaming full speed towards the open sea. The captain looked back ; that part of the harbour which he could see had been transformed. That morning any one looking down from the Peak would have seen the face of its waters covered with craft of all kinds—sampans, junks, coasting and deep-sea steamers, the channels through them which were kept clear for sea-going craft looking almost like lanes which have been cut through the tall reeds in a lake. Now all those vessels had gone—seeking safety. The face of the harbour, usually one of the most crowded in the world, was as deserted as a Highland loch in winter.

The clear spell did not last very long. Squall succeeded squall after they got outside, and the weather became rapidly worse, for the *Dulnain* had to get a good offing before she could start to make her southing, and while doing this she was of necessity steering almost straight toward the approaching typhoon. Fortunately during this time she had a following wind and sea, and made rapid progress. It is only near the centre of these tropical storms that the wind blows in concentric circles ; at their outer edges there seems to be a considerable indraft and the wind blows more toward the centre, thus making it fatally easy for any vessel to rush to her destruction. So threatening did the weather become that the captain was decidedly relieved when, having ran his distance, he was able to alter the *Dulnain's* course toward the south. He had had many anxious moments. The idea that he was steering straight toward the approaching disturbance, even for a short time, was rather unnerving ; it was almost like having to walk a certain distance along a railway line toward an approaching train, and he was glad to be able to turn away and steer at right angles to its probable course. With the wind more abeam, the *Dulnain* did not make such good progress, but every mile which she did make was in the right direction. Those on board spent a bad night. At daybreak it was still blowing half a gale, but the farther south they got the better the weather became, and the barometer was rising fast. By noon the wind and sea were moderate, and the sky had cleared ; by eight o'clock in the evening there was almost a dead calm.

That evening about nine o'clock the captain, clad in his pyjamas, was sitting in his cabin smoking. He had shaved, had a hot bath, and afterwards had dined well ; now he had that delightful feeling of comfort which comes to one who has backed his judgment, taken a risk, and seen it come off. He had been through rather a bad time ; for two days and a night he had not had his clothes off or been in bed, but now he considered that his vessel was safe. By his action in coming to sea he had saved at least two days, a saving which doubtless his owners would appreciate, and, moreover, he was now in fine weather, whereas the vessels which had remained in Hong Kong would probably be still using their engines to prevent them from dragging as they strained at their anchors, for the sheltering places there mainly protected them against the heavy seas. They would be feeling almost the full effect of the wind, especially those which were, like the *Dulnain*, in ballast trim, standing up like great balloons, and with little grip of the water.

How well his cheroot was drawing! He was lingering over the last few puffs with an eye all the time on his cosy bed. He had just been up on the bridge, written up his night order-book, and seen that the vessel was on a safe course. There was nothing to prevent him turning in and having a really good night's sleep. His cheroot being finished, he stretched himself luxuriously, switched off the light, and clambered into his bunk. In a few minutes he was sleeping like a log.

II.

At midnight the second officer, yawning heavily, ascended the bridge ladder for the purpose of keeping the middle watch. As he reached the bridge he noticed that the vessel was rolling slightly to an unseen swell, and he gazed around suspiciously, for drizzling rain was driving under the awning which had been stretched that afternoon. The sky, which had been quite clear at eight o'clock, was now overcast, and lightning was playing about low down on the horizon. The third officer gave him the course, and he took over the bridge while the former went into the chart-room to write up the bridge log-book. After a good look round to satisfy himself that there was nothing in the way, the second officer also went to the chart-room and leant against the open door.

" How long has the weather been like this ? " he asked.

" You mean the rain ? " replied the third, looking up from the log-book. " It came on about half an hour ago. Read the barometer for me like a good chap."

The reason for this request was that the mercurial barometer, the reading of which he had to enter in the log, was hanging close to the chart-room door against which the second officer was leaning, and the latter, automatically raising his hand to the adjusting screw of the vernier, was proceeding to read it when an astonished exclamation escaped him.

" Here, what the devil is this ? " he cried.

" What the devil is what ? "

" When did you read this glass last ? "

" At ten o'clock, of course," replied the third. " Why ? "

" Did you set it then ? " asked the second.

" Of course I did. What's the matter with you ? "

" Matter ! " exclaimed the second. " There's a gap of nearly half an inch between the bottom of the vernier and the mercury, and a depression like a cup at the top of the column. That's what is the matter." He screwed the vernier down. " The reading is now 28.95," he said.

" Good Lord ! " exclaimed the startled third officer.

" Yes ! You may well say good Lord. Before you proceed to your ill-earned rest just call the old man and inform *him*. Then, after he has told you what he thinks of you, say that I don't like the look of the weather at all, and would crave his presence on the bridge *ek dum*. Go on, don't argue, buzz off."

In less than three minutes—he did not seem to have wasted any time on the third officer—the captain, having slipped on his bridge coat over his pyjamas, had joined the second officer, and was

peering anxiously round the horizon. Just as he
reached the bridge the *Dulnain* gave a heavier roll.

" Good gracious ! " he said. " Why wasn't I
called long before this ? When did the third officer
notice that the glass was falling ? "

" I don't think that he looked at it since he read
it for the log-book at ten o'clock, sir."

" H'm ! I shall have to talk to that young man.
Reading the barometer only once every two hours
won't do for the China Sea in the typhoon season.
However, let's study the situation."

There was no mistaking the signs : the long rolling swell coming from the east, the short gusts
bringing with them that fine rain, and more especially the rapid fall of the barometer, could only
point to one thing—the approach of a cyclonic
storm.

" I have never known, or read, of a typhoon
recurving so far to the south as this one seems to
have done, sir," remarked the second officer.

" Are you talking about the typhoon which we
were watching for in Hong Kong ? " replied the
captain. " That one is playing havoc somewhere
up in the Formosa Channel by now. This is an
entirely fresh one, and it's going to be a damned
bad one too by the way the glass has dropped."

A long and anxious conversation followed. The
first thing they had to do was to ascertain the exact
direction of the wind, generally a rather difficult
job in a steamer owing to the complication introduced by her own movement through the water.
There was a moon which showed feeble and shape-
less—and surrounded by a large halo—through the

clouds, and by studying the direction in which those were passing over they were able to form a fair estimate as to how the wind was blowing. Facing the wind in imagination, and allowing about ten or twelve points of the compass to the right, they obtained the approximate bearing of the centre, and this was corroborated by the ever-increasing swell which they felt certain would be coming from the direction in which the storm was approaching, and would travel more rapidly than the storm centre. The tracks of a good many of those storms which had occurred in the past have been charted, and a study of the storm-chart, combined with the deductions which they had already made, convinced them that this one had probably developed somewhere to the south of the Philippine Islands, and was travelling in a north-westerly direction towards the Gulf of Tonquin.

If the conclusions which they had come to were correct, the *Dulnain* was somewhat to the north of the estimated line of approach of the typhoon, and that being so, but for one well-known fact, it would have been more prudent to have turned away north again to avoid the terrible centre bearing down on top of them. That fact was that there was no record of one of those storms having recurved to the south, whereas they frequently did to the north ; and if this one did so after they had turned back, they would be in a rather nasty position. Taking everything into consideration, their safest plan seemed to be to try and run across its estimated line of progression, and keep on trying to get away to the south. The captain adopted

this plan all the more readily, as the course chosen
led toward his port of destination. Always a
thruster, he lost few chances of getting on, although
he would not have hesitated to turn back had it
been really necessary to do so. Fortunately, there
was plenty of sea room, the only obstruction anywhere near them being the Tongs reef, and that
lay a day's steam to the south-east, and so far off
their track that it was hardly worth bothering
about.

"We re in for a severe dusting before we get
clear of this," said the captain, as he emerged from
the chart-room after their deliberations and looked
round. "You had better take a turn round the
deck and see that everything is secure. First of
all, have this awning furled."

The *Dulnain* was now rolling heavily to the
swell, the gusts of wind were coming at shorter
intervals, and with each gust the rain became
heavier. Between the gusts there were calm periods
when the atmosphere was sultry, heavily oppressive,
and moist. The most casual observer could hardly
fail to realise the threat of the coming storm.

Daybreak revealed a dense black bank of cloud
away out on the starboard beam. It came on like
a wall, sweeping over the water toward them, and
moaning as it came. The wind suddenly freshened
with a roar to the strength of a full gale, and seemed
to be tearing great jagged clouds from the bank
and flinging them across the sky. The sea began to
run high and cross, being now driven by the wind
into the teeth of the previous swell; and the sky
had a wild and terrifying appearance all day as the

Dulnain, labouring heavily, struggled to the south. Being so high out of the water no heavy seas came on board, but with the beam wind she was making several points of leeway. It was impossible to keep her on her proper course ; she was carrying the helm hard-a-port the whole time, but refused to go any higher into the wind. The sun was, of course, invisible, so that no observations could be taken. The captain's chief anxiety was caused by the fact that the wind never changed in direction ; it blew ominously true the whole day, which could only indicate that the vessel was right on the line of progression of the approaching centre. There was nothing else for it, however ; to turn back and run north now would be to court disaster ; he could only hold on and hope that the wind would eventually change.

It commenced to do so about eight o'clock in the evening, in such a manner as to indicate that they had got across the track of the storm at last, and that the centre would pass to the north of them. By that time the storm was almost at its worst, and the *Dulnain* was now engaged in a veritable battle of the elements, sea and sky being literally mingled together, for the fury of the irresistible blasts was cutting the tops off the towering seas and flinging them into the air in spray to mix with the torrential driving rain. It was so dark that no one could see a yard through the smother thus caused ; no look-out was possible, and the vessel had to drive blindly on, for to slow down or stop at that stage would have been fatal. Owing to the fury of the wind no man could move upright about

the deck, and once the captain was pinned for about
five minutes against the chart-room, breathless and
unable to move, his curses cut short at their source.
The quartermaster at the wheel had difficulty in
clinging to it, and could only do so by hanging on
to windward, so that he was practically jammed on
top of it. There was much lightning and probably
thunder, but the latter was inaudible in the roar of
the wind, which resembled that of an express train
emerging from a tunnel.

By nine o'clock they must have been very near
the centre, for the hurricane-like gusts were coming
from various directions, while the sea was boiling
and rising in great confused lumps and throwing
itself in all directions. The *Dulnain* was labouring
very heavily, and was being tossed about like a
cork. There was hardly a man on board either on
deck or below who had not some cut or bruise to
show, so violently were they being flung about, as
the vessel seemed to stand almost on her head at
one moment, and immediately afterwards slide
down the side of a leaning sea until she appeared to
be going over. Once clear of this region the weather
for the first time showed signs of improvement ;
and by midnight the barometer was rising a little,
the squalls had become slightly less violent and
were occurring at lengthening intervals, and the
sea, although still dangerously high, was beginning
to run true. By three o'clock in the morning the
wind had settled down into a hard gale from exactly
the opposite direction to that from which it had
been blowing the previous day.

Their troubles were, however, by no means over,

for shortly before dawn the engines stopped. The chief engineer sent a message to the bridge to say that a crank pin bottom-end bearing had run hot, that he would take steps to remedy it as soon as possible, but that work on it was very difficult owing to the heavy sea. The *Dulnain*, although still labouring heavily, was behaving more comfortably than she had done since the storm commenced. Being higher out of the water forward than she was aft, her head paid off as soon as she lost steerage-way, and she was now lying with the wind and sea on the port quarter, half rolling, half pitching, and drifting fast to leeward. It was still blowing too hard for them to attempt to hoist the lights usually displayed by a vessel not under command, but daylight was not very far away. The captain and chief officer—haggard, eyes dazed and bloodshot from want of sleep and with striving to pierce the smother of spray and driving rain—were huddled together under the lee of the chart-room waiting for it. When it came it revealed a sea of huge white-capped waves and a sky clear of clouds, save for a low grey bank which rose above the horizon to the eastward. The upper edge of the bank began to be rimmed with gold, the sun was rising, and the clear sky gave promise that later on they would be able to get observations. It was still blowing a hard gale, but nothing like what they had previously experienced—there were no longer the squalls of hurricane strength. They were thankful to feel that at last the worst was over.

"Well," said the captain, "it looks as if we were about finished with it. I wonder how long it will take the old chief to get the engines moving again. We can't do anything now except to lash the two black balls in the main rigging to show that we are broken down, although I don't expect that we shall sight anything." He yawned and stretched himself, for all his joints were stiff. " I think that the time is right for a spot of coffee. I will go down below and have some, and then——"

" *Breakers on the starboard bow.*"

The hail came from the man on the look-out, who was at his post in the crow's-nest half-way up the foremast. Incredulously the captain dived into the chart-room, pulled his binoculars out of a drawer where he had placed them to keep them dry, for they had been quite useless up till now, and stared through them to leeward. For a time he could make out nothing, for every wave was crowned with a white horse, which the look-out man might have mistaken for breakers ; but gazing in the direction in which that individual was pointing, he saw two columns of spray being flung high into the air, and eventually at the base of the columns he detected black rocks.

III.

The very first glimpse of those rocks revealed to the experienced eye of the captain the fact that his ship was in a desperate position, and that the lives of all on board were in deadly peril. The rocks were about three miles away, dead to leeward, directly in line with the wind. At the speed at which the *Dulnain* was drifting, she must in half an hour go crashing on top of them, when she would rapidly grind herself to pieces. Even if she missed the rocks themselves, she must hit the reef, which they marked, for they could not be standing up alone and unattached to anything in the middle of the ocean ; in either case her fate would be the same. He turned to the chief officer.

" Tell the second officer to come up here at once," he said. A brief glance to leeward followed. " In fact, call all hands," he added ominously.

During the absence of the chief officer from the bridge, he anxiously studied the rocks through his glasses, and took a bearing of them. There were two of them standing up like pinnacles, one slightly higher than the other, and they seemed to be the outlying sentries of a fairly large reef, which he could see covered with white churning foam beyond them. The chief officer quickly returned, followed shortly afterwards by the second.

" Turn up the ' Sailing Directions for the South China Sea ' and see what it says about the Tongs," the captain said to the latter.

" The Tongs, sir," questioned the officer with an astonished voice.

" Yes, the Tongs," replied the captain testily. " Damn it, man, what else can it be ? We allowed a lot for leeway yesterday when the wind was from the west, but evidently not enough by sixty miles. In fact, we have been blown to the eastward of the reef, and now we are being blown back again."

The second officer entered the chart-room, found the required book, and turned over the pages hastily, while the captain stood with a foot on either side of the doorstep.

" Here it is," said the former. " ' The Tongs reef,' " he read out, " ' about five cables long from north to south, and three cables wide from east to west. Marked on the south-east edge by two pinnacle rocks, one 87 feet in height, the other 59. These are steep-to. Well out of the ordinary track of shipping, and——' "

" Are they ? " interrupted the captain drily. " Well, there they are, anyhow. Steep-to, eh ? That means that an anchor is useless, but it gives us a better chance of clearing them. Simpson, give my compliments to the chief engineer, and ask him if he can possibly give us the engines even for ten minutes. Explain the situation to him. If he can't do it, well——" The captain shrugged his shoulders expressively, and going to the standard compass, he took another bearing of the rocks, which were now much nearer. The bearing had not altered, showing that they were driving straight for them.

"The chief says that he will do his best to give you the engines, sir," reported Simpson on his return, "but he is afraid that he can't drive them very fast. He will ring up when he is ready."

"Right ; let's hope that he won't be very long," said the captain. "There is one other chance, but a very poor one—set the try-sails. With this strong wind they might give us steerage-way, and if they did that much it might help. They will also steady her. Set the main one first—it will keep her head up to the wind."

Calling all the deck hands together the chief officer made his way aft, and the main try-sail was loosed. While this was being done it showed visible signs of distress, and no wonder. With the gale which was still blowing nothing but a storm-sail of good No. 0 canvas would have stood. The try-sail was nothing like as strong as that, and moreover it was by no means new, with the result that no sooner had the hands hauled the sheet of it taut and belayed it than the sail was torn from its surrounding ropes, and went hurtling bodily to leeward in the direction of the rocks. The chief officer again appeared on the bridge.

"Main try-sail blown away, sir," he reported.

"I saw it," replied the captain. "Leave the fore one alone or it will go the same way."

By this time they had got so close that the dull roar of the great combers dashing against the base of the rocks could be heard above the whistle of the wind. Those on the bridge began to think that even if they got the engines now it would be too late—they would strike before way could be got on the ship. The sailors were clustered on the fore-deck, well aware of their peril. From the bridge two of them could be seen lugging their sea-chests out through the forecastle door, though what they expected to do with them was not very clear. The engine-room telegraph clanged—the indicator from below had moved to ' stand by.'

" Engines ready, sir," shouted the third officer.

" Right, full speed ahead," ordered the captain. " He can't give us full speed, I know," he added, " but we will take all that he *can* give us."

It was evident to him that it was quite useless to try to turn the vessel's head to wind and steam away from the rocks. Long before he could get her round she would be on top of them, and in any case he would probably not get enough power from the engines to enable her to stem the wind and sea. The wind was about due east and the rocks were bearing west. He would try to steer south—at right angles to both ; and if he could get way enough on the *Dulnain* she might possibly slip clear.

" Hard-a-starboard, quartermaster," he ordered. " Let me know when she answers her helm."

Very slowly she commenced to gather way ; it seemed an age before the quartermaster reported that she was coming round. The second officer stood at the standard compass watching for an alteration in the bearing of the rocks.

" Steady her on south, quartermaster," said the captain, as the vessel's head began perceptibly to swing to port.

" South it is, sir," replied the quartermaster cheerily. The sight of him stolidly spinning the hitherto useless wheel had a reassuring effect on the little group on the bridge.

The eyes of all hands were riveted on the rocks, now only a cable's length away on the starboard beam, and still drawing nearer. Whatever speed the *Dulnain* was making ahead, and she barely appeared to be crawling, she was certainly making four knots sideways, to leeward.

" Is she altering the bearing at all ? " the captain asked anxiously.

" Very hard to say, sir ; the compass card is swinging so much. Yes, sir, nearly a point," shouted the second officer.

The *Dulnain*, now beam on to the sea, was again rolling heavily as she slowly slid past the rocks. Now they would appear above the level of the rail ; a moment afterwards they would be deep down in the trough of the sea. The large combers were alternately dashing at their bases to throw showers of spray high into the air, or rushing at them green, almost covering the top of the smaller one. Between the pinnacles and stretching to the north-west was the reef itself, a white cauldron of foam. To the south-west—in which direction the combined actions of the engines moving ahead, and the wind and sea driving her sideways, would probably take the vessel—the sea seemed clear.

" She's altering the bearing quickly now, sir,"

shouted the second officer excitedly. But, indeed, the rocks were now so close that watching the compass bearing was quite unnecessary. They were well abaft the beam, but the gap between them and the ship was closing all too quickly. Every wave that rushed at the *Dulnain* seemed to throw her nearer to them. All hands on deck were watching them in suspense ; the officers on the bridge, with breaths hard held, were clinging firmly to the rails, their gaze ever shifting in direction farther aft ; another fifty feet on and, if there were no outlying spurs, the vessel would be clear. Just then a man emerged from the saloon door at the break of the poop. It was the chief steward—a corpulent Frenchman,— who had either been forgotten when all hands had been called, or, what was more likely from his well-known habits, had been called and gone off to sleep again. He was clad only in his shirt, and for a few seconds stood stretching himself ; then his attention was apparently attracted by the roar of the breakers to the rocks, which were by that time just abreast of where he stood, and now barely half a cable distant. For a moment he gazed at them as if petrified, then, barefooted, with almost incredible activity, he dashed forward along the leaning deck, climbed the iron ladder at the after end of the lower bridge, and came flying along it shouting as he came. When near enough for his voice to be heard he stopped, and waving his arms forward with the motion of one directing a tug-of-war team, he shouted at the pitch of his voice—

" Full speed ahead, *capitan*, full speed ahead. *Vitement pour l'amour de Dieu, vitement.*"

At that moment the rocks seemed to dive under the *Dulnain's* stern. The steward, gesticulating wildly, continued to shout his exhortations. The third officer was the first to laugh—he commenced with a nervous giggle ; the second followed with a deep guffaw. The captain, who usually had the keenest sense of humour of them all, also commenced to laugh, then suddenly checked himself ; he felt that it would take very little to make him hysterical, and fearing to disgrace himself before his officers and his crew, he turned resolutely away and studied the sea to leeward with his glasses on the look-out for any outlying portions of the reef. The chief officer had crossed to the other side of the bridge, and was therefore the only one among them who saw the rocks reappear again—this time on the weather quarter,—and who noticed the ever-widening lane of tumbling water between them and the *Dulnain*, now driving fast into safety. He swiftly recrossed the bridge and joined the captain.

" By God, sir, she's cleared them," he shouted.

The captain apparently took no notice ; he continued to stare to leeward, swallowing hard and pulling himself together. Then instead of answering the chief officer, he leant over the after-rail, and addressed the still excited steward.

" Steward," he said, " when you've quite finished saving the ship, would you mind telling the cook to get coffee ready for all hands—they will need it. Also please go away at once and dress yourself properly ; you are positively indecent."

The little group of officers was standing on the bridge watching the reef swiftly receding to wind-

ward, and each one busy with his own thoughts,
when suddenly the engine-room telegraph clanged
again.

" What's that ? " asked the captain sharply.

" Engines stopped, sir," replied the third officer,
as he jerked the telegraph handle to give the answering signal.

" Heavens ! what a let off. Well, it doesn't
much matter now. Give my compliments to the
chief engineer, and tell him that we have cleared
the reef and he can carry on with his repairs. We
are three hundred miles from the nearest land, and
it will take a devil of a time to drift that distance,
so he can take his time and make a good job of it."

The captain suddenly felt very tired and shaky,
and it was little wonder. Since they had left Hong
Kong, three days before, he had had barely four
hours' sleep ; indeed during most of the time he
had been on the bridge. In addition, the strain of
the last hour had been terrific. He went into the
chart-room, took his case from an inside pocket,
found a dry box of matches, and, lighting a cigarette, sat down on the settee, puffing luxuriously.
The chief officer followed him, and from force of
habit began to write up the bridge log-book. The
captain eyed him curiously, and wondered if he
himself looked anything like that. The usually
calm and immaculate officer was unshaven, haggard,
and white, his face grimed with dry salt from the
stinging spray. The hand that held the pen shook
so much that he could not write. He eventually
gave up trying, laid the pen down, and, shaking his
head wearily, looked at his superior.

"Well, Simpson," said the latter, "a quarter of an hour ago I would have given fifty to one that I had smoked my last cigarette. We can't come to any harm now. Leave the third officer up here and you and the second come down to my cabin. Coffee is most decidedly indicated, and if we *do* add a liberal dash of brandy and make a coffee-royal of it, well, it won't do us the slightest harm."

SAIL BEATS STEAM.

I. THE ENGLISH CHANNEL, 1895.

ONE morning in April 1895 the large clipper ship on which I was an apprentice lay becalmed off Start Point. We were homeward bound from Iquique to Dunkirk, and up to the time of approaching the Channel had made an excellent passage. We had carried favourable winds from the coast of Chile right round the Horn to the Line ; by great good luck we had had practically no doldrums, having lost the south-east Trades and picked up the north-east in the one squall. The north-east Trades had been succeeded by strong westerly winds ; indeed, from the Azores we had been scudding before them with as much canvas set as we could stagger under. Visions of a record passage came to us, but all of a sudden, in the vicinity of the Scilly Islands, the brave westerlies died away, to be succeeded by a light north-east wind—almost a dead muzzler up-Channel. Even this had now failed us, and left a calm in its wake.

To any one not engaged in trying to make a passage in a sailing ship it was a glorious morning. The sky was cloudless, though low down on the horizon there lay a haze. The sea was like a sheet

F

of glass, but a gentle swell was rolling up from the south-west, causing the vessel to pitch slightly. Her useless canvas hung straight up and down, except when a heavier pitch than usual would cause it to slat heavily against the masts. Partly to avoid this, the lower sails, the courses, were hauled up.

We were all looking forward to the end of the voyage, and anxious to get to our homes after an absence of fifteen months, so to be stopped like this, within a day's sail of our port, was disappointing. After all, however, a few more days meant little difference to us, whereas to the captain it most decidedly did ; his professional reputation and his standing with his owners greatly depended on the passages he made. It was little wonder, therefore, that he was in a vile temper as he walked up and down the poop, now pausing to gaze round the horizon and whistle vainly for a breeze, again stopping to curse at any one within reach in whose work he had detected some shortcoming. We apprentices had already felt the rough edge of his tongue while handling the flags in an attempt to make our number off the Start. It was not our fault that there was no wind to make the flags stand out, but he apparently did not entirely acquit us of blame.

Coming up behind, but rather closer into the land, was a tramp steamer with a red funnel with black top. When about a mile away on our port quarter she hoisted her number and ensign, which was acknowledged by the answering pennant on the flagstaff of the signal station. Before the signal was hauled down our old man had got his telescope on to it and read the flags.

" Hand me that signal book, one of you," he ordered.

I jumped for the book, and he rapidly turned over its pages until he found the steamer's name.

" The *Ripon* of London," he exclaimed. " That's the boat my brother is in command of ; at least he was there when I heard of him last. Curse those flags, why won't they blow out so that he could see them."

His brother had, however, apparently recognised the ship without the flags, for we could see the steamer's course altered so that she would pass close to us. She did not ease down as she approached ; the etiquette of the merchant service and the owner's interests would not permit of that, but she passed within easy hail.

" Hullo, Bob, where are you bound to ? " shouted her skipper when she got near enough.

" Hullo, Bill, Dunkirk," was the reply.

" Good, so am I. Made a good passage ? "

" Very good up to the Scillys. I have been six blasted days from there to here."

" Hard luck." By this time the steamer was drawing away.

" Well, see you in Dunkirk," shouted our old man.

" Perhaps, but not at your present rate of progression," was the reply. " I've only got eight thousand tons to discharge there. Bye-bye."

At this piece of sarcasm our old man shook his fist in the direction of his brother, then turned with a despairing gesture and gazed toward the western horizon. There seemed to be nothing there that pleased him, for he resumed his pacing up and down the poop, pausing once to swear at the young third mate for some supposed dereliction of duty. Occasionally with a gloomy eye he would note the progress of the *Ripon* as she ploughed her way up-Channel; then tired of his walking he sat down moodily on the wheel-box grating. Suddenly a light puff of wind and a dark ripple on the water to the south-west galvanised him into action. The vessel was lying with square yards, and at the time her head was idly pointing to the south-east.

" Port fore brace," he shouted. " Lively now; get the other yards round as soon as you can, and sheet home the courses." Then, as she gathered headway, to the man at the wheel, who ten minutes before he had called a squareheaded idiot—

" East by south, my lad."

Cheerfully we had jumped to carry out his orders, and soon with the yards well trimmed and every foot of canvas drawing to the light breeze on the quarter, she was leaning over slightly, while the sea rippled pleasantly past her sides. After about ten minutes of this there was an ominous flap of the canvas aloft; sorrowfully we noted that the sea had become glassy again, and the wind had died away. It was, however, a false alarm; puff succeeded puff from the same direction; the ship never lost steerage-way, and eventually the surface of the sea to windward became an unbroken series of tiny wavelets. Gradually these grew larger, and their crests began to break. By noon, when our

watch on deck ended and we went below to our
pea-soup and salt pork, she was streaking along at
eight knots, the wind was still freshening, and the
sky gave every promise of more.

We came on deck again at four o'clock to find
that this promise had been fulfilled, and that we
required our oilskins and sea-boots. Ragged clouds
flew fast overhead ; a thin drizzle had come along
on the wind, making it difficult to see more than a
few miles ; and the spray was flying over the
weather rail. The tall vessel presented an exhilarat-
ing spectacle ; she was now leaning over heavily,
and the short, stiff, Channel waves coming up on
her quarter would occasionally roll her over to leeward with a lurch which would almost put the lee
rail awash and cause the water to gush in through
the scupper holes. Aloft every stitch of canvas,
now dark and sodden with the rain, was doing its
duty nobly, straining at bolt ropes and at sheets,
while the weather rigging would twang like harp-
strings as she lurched. Two men were at the wheel,
for she was yawing heavily as she tore along in a
broad smother of foam. We hove the log before
going below at six o'clock, and found that she was
doing twelve knots.

We apprentices of the starboard watch were a
cheerful little gang when we sat down on our sea-
chests in the little half-deck for tea in the second
dog-watch. The day before had been ' whack '
day, when our week's allowance of sugar and marma-
lade had been issued. Usually with all due care
we could make these last for nearly five days ; now
we dived into them with reckless prodigality. With

any luck we might be at home before the next whack day came round.

" Now this is just right," said the senior apprentice, as he lit his filthy briar which he had filled with black plug tobacco, and lay back on his sea-chest with his feet against another to brace him against the lurches. " The old man is so wild with his brother that he will crack on all night. He has been sailing this packet a bit too carefully for my liking lately." From his superior altitude of almost three years' service the senior apprentice felt quite capable of criticising the seamanship of any one.

" You didn't say that when he was cracking on that night off the Western Islands, and had to call all hands to get the sail off her," piped the auburn-haired youngest apprentice.

" Now you shut up, ' Copper-top,' or I'll be under the painful necessity of getting up and dotting you one. How often have I told you that first voyagers should be seen and not heard ? "

' Copper-top ' subsided with a cheerful grin. If the wind held the voyage might be over by to-morrow, and when another one started he could no longer be designated a first voyager.

It was dark when we came on deck again at eight o'clock, to find the lofty vessel still storming her way up-Channel through the murk and gloom. Away on our port quarter we could see one of the shore lights on the south coast of England winking cheerfully through the rain. We were still carrying every stitch of canvas, and although this may have seemed foolhardy, and due, as the senior apprentice had suggested, to the old man's annoyance at his brother's last remark, we knew that the former knew what he was doing. It was his duty to his owners to take advantage of the fair wind and get his vessel into port as soon as he could ; he had his chance, and he meant to take it. Clad in a sou'-wester, long black oilskin coat and sea-boots, with his night-glasses suspended from a leather strap round his neck, he was keeping his vigil on the weather side of the poop. Swaying easily as the vessel lurched, he would make his way to the binnacle to see how she was heading, and then to the rail, where he would peer to windward as if trying to estimate the strength of the wind, following this by a glance aloft to see how the sails were standing the strain. Carefully he examined every light that was reported. Self-reliant, competent, and wholly trustworthy, he looked what he was, a perfect type of the British sailing-ship captain. Those shrewd blue eyes which, despite himself, could not restrain a kindly twinkle, even as he swore, had for years been steadfastly regarding all the dangers of the seven seas.

Strange to say, there was no sheet of water on the ocean that the windjammer sailor dreaded so much as his own English Channel, and the reason is not far to seek. Nowhere else can such traffic be found, and this traffic, suddenly encountered after leagues and leagues of lonely sea, had an unnerving effect. The look-out on the forecastle head had been doubled, but in addition to that every soul in the watch was voluntarily acting in that capacity. Mustered under the break of the poop, where we were handy to carry out any orders, we would peer

over the weather rail as well as we could with the
driving rain and spray, then slide down the leaning
deck and gaze in the direction of the English coast,
trying to identify the various lights whether on
shore or on vessels.

We passed several steamers bound the same way,
which is not to be wondered at, for in those days
comparatively few tramp steamers could do ten
knots, while we averaged twelve all through the
watch, and in some of the squalls must have been
doing close on fourteen. We hoped that the *Ripon*
was amongst them, but had no means of knowing ;
at that time Morse code signalling was not practised
in the merchant service as it is to-day. We were
responsible for keeping out of the way of fishermen
with their nets down, and of other sailing vessels
which were close-hauled beating down-Channel ;
everything else had to keep clear of us, but we were
by no means certain that they would do so. Never
had our side-lights been more closely attended.
Once a cross-Channel steamer, evidently trusting to
his superior speed, tried to cross our bow, while we
helplessly watched him in breathless suspense.
The second mate, not even accepting the assurance
of the men on the look-out that the starboard light
was burning brightly, dashed forward, and as he
leant over the side to examine it, we could see his
face assume a ghastly green colour in its glare.
Just in time those in charge of the steamer must
have realised that we were tearing along much
faster than they had imagined ; they were too late
to come under our stern, so had to turn away and
make a complete circle before getting on their

course again. At midnight, when the watch was relieved, the conditions were unchanged ; the last glimpse which I had of the old man revealed him with his arm round a weather backstay to steady himself, while he studied some light with his glasses.

All excitement although we were, our young heads had hardly touched the pillows in our bunks before we were in a deep slumber. For months we had never had as much as four hours' sleep at a time, and in consequence we knew how to take advantage of every moment. One bell, a quarter to four, came all too soon, but we certainly tumbled out on this occasion with greater alacrity than usual.

The old man was still where we had last seen him before we went below. The traffic was increasing as we drew up towards the straits, and when daylight broke the grand old cliffs of Dover lay along our lee beam. In the moving panorama of shipping were many types which have since disappeared. Sailing pilot boats from various continental ports darted to and fro ; coasting brigs and schooners were everywhere ; closer in-shore one of the famous colonial clippers was towing down-Channel, and we suddenly had to alter course and go under the stern of a large American full-rigged ship, with black wooden hull and snow-white cotton canvas sails, which, close-hauled, was endeavouring to beat to the westward. We were in high spirits. There is nothing in the life of the steamboat sailor of to-day to compare with a fresh morning in the Channel on a sailing-ship with a fair wind—homeward bound.

The weight had gone out of the wind, but we were still making good progress. About three hours afterwards we picked up the Dyck Lightship, which is about fifteen miles from Dunkirk, and very shortly afterwards hove-to to take on board the sturdy French pilot from the Dunkirk pilot boat.

" Do you think we can manage to dock this tide ? " was our captain's first question.

" But yes," was the reply. " Square away the yards ; by-and-by catch the tug-boat. Dock this tide, *certainement*."

We were soon on our course again, but the wind was beginning to die down, when, fortunately for us, a Dunkirk tug ranged alongside, and, after a little less haggling than usual, she passed us her hawser. All the sails were clewed up, and we went aloft to furl them. As the senior apprentice and I were putting a harbour stow on the mizzen-royal we gazed ahead toward our port. From that height we could see the docks at Dunkirk with the masts of the shipping, the town itself, and the fair land of France beyond.

" Hullo, there's brother Bill's old puffing Billy," exclaimed my companion, who professed a profound contempt for steam. I looked in the direction in which he was pointing, and there, about six miles astern, was the red-and-black funnel of the *Ripon*. We were about to shout this information down to the poop when we noticed that the old man had already got his telescope on to her.

With the little tug bravely towing ahead we made for the entrance to the docks. From the basin we warped along to our berth, and, as we trudged

round the capstan, pushing on the bars, one of the
crew struck up the old chantey which was always
reserved for the last day of the voyage—

"The times are hard and the wages are low,
 Leave her, Johnny—leave her."

French stevedores, dock labourers, and the usual
loungers about a port stopped to listen as its plaintive air re-echoed round the docks. It is strange
how plaintive the airs of all those old chanteys
were—even those which were meant to be sung in
moments of triumph such as this.

We hove alongside the quay and moored the
ship securely to it. The hands were coiling up the
ropes, doing the last few odd jobs about the deck,
and waiting for the quiet " That will do, men " from
the mate, which would make them free men again
after months of toil on the restless sea, and the
nitrate ports of Chile, when the *Ripon* entered the
dock and began hauling in to her berth. We could
see her captain on the bridge staring across at us,
but at first there was no sign of our old man. Before
long, however, he came on to the poop, took a few
turns fore and aft, and then, on his way forward,
drew himself up with an exaggerated start of surprise as he apparently noticed the *Ripon* for the
first time.

" Hullo," he shouted to his brother, " are you
still here ? "

There was no answer. We saw his brother walk
across to the other side of the bridge and look along
the quay as if he were taking an interest in the

mooring. He then came back and had another look at us, and as he did so our old man fired another question at him.

" You look very deep in the water. Have you discharged that eight thousand tons yet ? "

His brother picked up his megaphone and, breathless, we awaited his reply. It came booming across the intervening stretch of water in the dock, and fell on our delighted ears. It was not an answer to our old man's question ; it was more in the nature of an order. It was brief and picturesque, and was couched in real seamanlike language. I would like to give it here, but refrain—it would not look so well in print.

II. THE HAMMAR LAKE, 1915.

I.

By the middle of August 1915, the problem of river transport between Nasiriyah, on the Euphrates, and the base at Basra had become rather an involved one. The operations for the capture of that city had been in the nature of a race against time and the falling Hammar Lake, but they had been successfully concluded ; all the large paddle-steamers had gone down with the wounded, and were now plying on the Tigris. There was still, however, the greater part of a division to be maintained and supplied at Nasiriyah.

In this river transport there were four stages, each requiring a different method. The first was from Nasiriyah to the Akaika bund, and the river there, although narrow, was fairly deep ; the second was the narrow channel, or rapid, through the obstruction, and this had been widened and made much easier to pass through than it had been when we had first gone up. Then came the lake itself, which was the worst of all, for the water in its tortuous channel had shoaled to two feet, and was still shoaling, while the fourth stage, from

Kubaish, at the eastern end of the lake, to Kurna, where the Euphrates joined the Tigris and formed the Shatt-el-Arab, was easy, the river being both wide and deep.

A fairly satisfactory system was arranged, which worked quite well until the lake became too shallow for anything but native boats, the large iron barges of Lynch & Company being used throughout. Between Nasiriyah and the bund they were towed by small, but rather deep, twin-screw tugs, which plied between these places only. They were hauled up or lowered down the narrow channel in the obstruction by men from an Indian regiment who were stationed there for the purpose, and then towed across the lake by shallow draft stern-wheel steamers. Between Kubaish and Kurna they were towed by one of the large paddlers. These barges, when regularly used for the transport of troops, were covered with awnings, and were fairly comfortable, at least as comfortable as anywhere else in that blistering land at that time of the year.

About this time the mixed British and Indian machine-gun battery which I was then commanding at Nasiriyah received orders to proceed to the Tigris to join the other division. Also under the same orders were a Gurkha battalion, a field battery, and a Territorial battalion, the only one then in the country. The Gurkhas left three days before we did. In what passed for the cool of the evening we struck camp, and embarked with all our gear on one of the iron barges. On the same barge was the field battery, while on another, which was banked in just above us, was the Territorial battalion. After seeing that all the gear was on board, and that the men were comfortable, we had dinner, and settled down for the night.

At daybreak one of the tugs came alongside. I was wakened by the noise, got up, and proceeded to watch with interest the antics of her commander. He was a half-caste of some sort, and was a non-commissioned officer, known in marine circles as a gunner. Clad in a comic khaki uniform, he was strutting up and down the bridge like a peacock, and it did not take me very long to discover that he knew very little about his job. Had it not been for the skill and activity of the Chaldean boatmen who manned the barges, it would have been hours before he got them secured alongside, but with their aid we managed to make a start within a reasonable time. The barges were lashed one on each side of the tug, and as they were much longer they projected beyond her at both ends.

The sun was just rising, and it was not yet hot when we started off down-stream. Most of us were in high spirits at leaving Nasiriyah, for that place had become a backwater, where little was expected to happen. The centre of activity had shifted to the Tigris, and rumour had it that there great events were pending. How great they would eventually turn out to be, or how tragic, none of us, fortunately, could foresee : there were very few on those barges, either officers or men, who were not destined to be dead or prisoners of war within the next nine months. We lay back contentedly, enjoying the morning air, and watching the fertile date plantations slipping past, thankful to be, for the time being, clear of dust and flies.

For a time all went well; then going round a bend the bow of one of the barges took the bank, with the result that the current swept the whole outfit, tug and barges, right round so that they were eventually heading up-stream again. This gave the comic gunner a chance to show how really incapable he was. Getting close into one bank he would order all the helms over; then go ahead on the engines, and before he knew what had happened we had shot across the stream, hit the bank on the other side with the same result as before, the current again caught us, and we were still heading up-stream. On the banks of the river were date plantations, and soon there were small gatherings of Arabs on both sides, evidently anxious for the safety of their flood banks, which the gunner seemed to have every intention of ramming. They expostulated angrily in Arabic with the Chaldean boatmen, who, with emphatic gestures, were disclaiming all responsibility. Every now and then one of them would jerk a contemptuous thumb toward the bridge of the tug where the gunner appeared to be trying to convert the engine-room telegraph into a chime of bells.

This sort of thing had been going on for about twenty minutes, and the spectacle of two batteries and a battalion, on barges, being rapidly rushed from one side of the Euphrates to the other and then back again had really become ridiculous. I was watching the proceedings with a certain amount of amusement, for time was of no object to me, when I was joined by the O.C. troops, who also happened to be a brigadier-general. He, of course, was anxious to get on.

" You seem to be rather amused," he remarked sourly. " I presume *you* would do a great deal better ? "

" I couldn't do much worse, sir," I replied.

" Well, suppose you go up and have a try."

" I could hardly do that, sir. It wouldn't do to take the boat out of her commander's hands."

" *What ?* " roared the brigadier, who had not yet had his breakfast. " I am O.C. here, and I order you to."

This put an entirely different complexion on it. Hastily saluting, I climbed on board the tug and mounted to the bridge. The gunner resented my presence, and clearly showed it ; and when I told him that I had been ordered to take charge he retired to one side of the bridge very much on his dignity. The necessary manœuvre was really very simple. Having ordered the helms of both barges and tug to be put over, and the engines easy ahead, I stopped them again as soon as the barges' heads were canted out from the bank. I then ordered the engines easy astern until the stern of one of the barges took the mud, when I stopped the engines and let the current do the rest. Catching the bow of the up-stream barge, it swept us round, and, as soon as we were heading down-stream, I ordered the engines full speed ahead, handed charge of the tug over to the gunner, and went back to my barge for breakfast.

I had just finished that meal, picked out a soft

spot on the deck, and got 'Martin Chuzzlewit,' my sole literary companion for weeks, out of my valise, when there was a bump that nearly threw us off our feet. One of the barges had again taken the mud, tug and barges were spinning round, and before long were again heading up-stream. I had been looking forward to a quiet read and a doze, but it was not to be : the O.C. troops had got his eye on me. Jerking his thumb in the direction of the bridge, he said—

"Up you go." Then he added as a sort of after-thought, "And you had better stay up there until we get down to Akaika, or we won't get there to-day."

Inwardly cursing whoever had informed him that I had been a sailor, I again took over from the gunner, turned round as simply as before, and pro-ceeded down-stream. I had little difficulty in keep-ing the tug in the middle of the river, and began to enjoy the trip. From the high bridge one could get a good view, and the country which we were passing through was the greenest and most fertile that I had seen in Mesopotamia. Mingled with the date plantations were rice-fields full of young seedlings, apparently not long transplanted. Dotted here and there were small villages, each with its square, loop-holed, mud tower, very similar to the tribal towers in certain parts of the North-West Frontier of India. The belt of cultivation extended for about a mile inland, then stopped abruptly at the edge of the desert, which stretched away to the horizon. Without further mishap we got down to Akaika, where I handed the vessels over to the

transport officer. The Gurkhas were still in camp
there ; they were a hospitable lot, and the officers
of the field battery and myself decided to pay them
a visit. It was during this gin crawl that the
trouble commenced.

We found the Gurkhas rather disgruntled. Some
genius had evolved the idea of sending troops
across the lake in *mashufs*, small sailing vessels of
the country of light draft manned by Arabs, who
knew every inch of the lake, and the Gurkhas were
to be the first to make the experiment. They were
starting in the morning, and were by no means
looking forward to spending a whole day in open
boats under the grilling August sun. A cheery
sapper major, a fellow-passenger in our barge, had
got to their mess tent before us, and, more I think
by way of making himself agreeable than because he
believed it, was assuring the colonel of the Gurkhas
that they would get to Kubaish before we would.

" Oh, nonsense," said the colonel gloomily.
" We probably won't fetch there at all, and even
if we do we will have casualties amongst the men
through heat stroke."

" I'll bet you fifty rupees, colonel, that you
arrive at Kubaish before we do."

" Money for nothing," said the colonel. " I'll
take you."

This started the betting, but it veered round
entirely the other way. Every one wished to back
his own mount, as it were, and soon every officer
in the battery, and one or two of the Territorials
who had also rolled up, had bets on with the Gurkha
officers that we should get across the lake before

them. I had taken no part in it, for in conversation
with the transport officer I had learned that the
stern-wheeler which was going to tow us across,
although she drew less water than the barges, had
had great difficulty in getting across from Kubaish
that day. Moreover, even if she could manage to
haul the barges through the mud, it would be
difficult to keep them straight, and it would be no
good forging ahead if heading at right angles to the
proper course. With this inside information I
would certainly have backed the *mashufs*, which
only drew a foot of water to the barge's two, but
for one thing. I realised that the O.C. troops had
come to the conclusion that I was either a heaven-
sent navigator, or a lazy fellow who required work,
and I was certain that at the first hitch on the
morrow I was for it again.

After a cheery hour with the Gurkhas and a few
spots of their excellent gin we returned to our
barges, had dinner, and turned in.

II.

Just after daybreak our barges were slacked
down through the opening in the obstruction by
the men of the double company of Indian infantry
who were stationed there, the stern-wheeler came
along, and the barges were lashed alongside of her.
Her skipper was a tall dignified Arab, who, according to the transport officer, was a good man, and I
could see that he evidently knew his job. As we
steamed down the mile of channel which led from

the bund to the lake, we passed the *mashufs* lined along the bank. The Gurkhas were busily engaged getting on their kit, and there was a light but steady breeze.

Our first difficulty arose shortly after we entered the lake, for we struck a patch of shoal water almost at once, and, as I anticipated, although the stern-wheeler could tow the barges through a few inches of mud at about two knots an hour, they refused to steer, and very shortly were heading across the channel. At first the O.C. troops did not notice what had happened, and when he did I had gone to the after end of the barge to see how the men were getting in. Before long he approached me and said quite nicely—

" I would be really obliged if you would go up and lend the skipper a hand."

What I had done yesterday in the way of turning the tug and barges round had been easy and obvious ; this was a different situation altogether, and as I mounted to the stern-wheeler's bridge, I felt that I could do nothing to cope with it. Moreover, the Arab skipper was a totally different type of man to the gunner ; he had probably commanded this same boat for years, whereas I had never handled a stern-wheeler in my life. He spoke Hindustani, and when I explained why I had come up, he courteously welcomed my assistance and stopped the engines. I was looking round wondering what to do next and feeling a fraud, when a very welcome reinforcement appeared. I heard a voice from the Territorials' barge say—

" May I come up ? "

It was an officer named F., afterwards captured at Kut, and known to fame as one of the Kastamouni Incorrigibles, whom I knew to be a keen yachtsman.

" Certainly," I replied.

F. said that he saw our difficulty, and thought that he could overcome it. He told me what he thought of doing, and I in turn explained it to the skipper, who was keen to try it. If I would lend him some of my men, he would get some of his, organise them in two gangs, arm them with two long stout poles which he had found on board, and post them at the after end of the barges. With the poles they would try to push the stern of the barges round the way I wanted them. When we were on our course I would signal to him, he would stop the pushing, and we could go ahead full speed on the engines. The plan acted well ; with a gang of the Territorials on one barge, and some of my heftiest Sikhs and Punjabi Mussalmans, aided by a few field gunners, on the other, we were soon on our course. When we fell away from it again the pushing had to be repeated. It was a slow and laborious proceeding, but we were making headway and always moving in the right direction. About then I noticed that the Gurkhas were under way, and coming down the channel toward the lake with a light fair wind. The sun was well up, and there was every indication of a sweltering day.

Soon afterwards the water deepened, we could dispense with the poling gangs, and were making fair progress. Perched on the bow of each barge was a blue-robed Chaldean boatman sounding with

a bamboo pole marked in feet. Their method of
reporting the depths of water was decidedly quaint.
When there was upward of three feet they chanted
cheerfully in Arabic, " *Neemuch moy*," meaning
" plenty of water." Three feet and two feet were
given in mixed Hindustani and English as " *teen*
foot " and " *do* foot," the latter with a note of
alarm, as it was just about the water we were drawing. When it got below the latter figure they
emitted a series of short grunts, following these
up, as the vessels gradually eased down and stuck,
by a prolonged howl of despair as if all were indeed
lost.

The skipper pointed out to me the general direction in which the rather narrow channel through
the lake lay, but said that it changed from day to
day. The lake was so shallow that it was dotted
all over with Marsh Arabs, who lived in mat huts
amongst the tall reeds which lined the shore and
the various islands, and who were wading about
after their water buffaloes. They were good aids
to navigation ; with field-glasses one could tell at
some distance how far they were immersed, and if
the water were up to a man's waist or a water
buffalow's flank, it was quite deep enough for us.
The buffaloes were not, however, always an in-
fallible guide, as I will show later. It was now a
flat calm, and the surface of the lake was like glass.
I looked back through my glasses at the *mashufs ;*
they were clustered together idly, their sails hanging
limply up and down the masts, and I pitied the
people on board of them. It was hot enough with
us even under awnings, and the glare on the water

was terrific. The Gurkha colonel's forebodings were being realised, and I began to think that he would win his bet after all, for the plan evolved by F. seemed to have proved our salvation.

The Arab skipper asked me if I would take charge while he went below for a meal. I assented, and for a time all went well. The leadsmen were cheerfully chanting their "*neemuch moy*," and all seemed plain sailing. Noticing a buffalo with only head and shoulders above water, I altered course slightly, so as to pass close to it, thinking that a little extra water under us would do no harm. Very soon there was a shout of "*teen* foot," followed by a startled "*do* foot" and the usual grunts, and I realised that we were getting out of the channel. As I rang the telegraph to put the engines astern, a movement which brought the skipper hastily back to the bridge, and called the attention of every officer on board, the brute of a buffalo suddenly rose to its feet, and I could see that he was standing in about a foot of water. Before that he had been lying down, and had wallowed a hole for himself in the mud. I felt a good deal of a fool, and my feelings were not improved by a conversation between the two barges which was evidently meant for my benefit. Said one of the gunner officers to a friend on the other barge—

" I say, George, the new skipper's eye seems to be out to-day."

" Never was in," replied George solemnly. " He's a dud."

It required F. and his pole gangs to get us straightened up again and back into the channel, and in

the meantime a breeze had come away from the
north-west, a fair wind for the *mashufs*, which were
now about five miles astern but fast coming on.
The race was by no means over yet, for even in
deep water the *mashufs* could sail much faster than
the stern-wheeler could tow the barges, if they got
a strong breeze. This was not long in coming, and
it brought with it quite a choppy sea, which caused
barges and stern-wheeler to jump about, and put
a heavy strain on the ropes with which they were
lashed together. At the eastern end of the lake we
again got into shallow water, the pole gangs had to
be requisitioned, and their work was rendered much
more difficult by the motion of the vessels and the
fact that the barges were bumping heavily on the
bottom. Our progress was painfully slow.

By now the *mashufs*, leaning over heavily, were
coming on at a good pace, each with a smother of
foam at the bow. Circumstances, however, began
to favour us again. Through the reeds, which were
eight to ten feet high, at the end of the lake, a
broad opening appeared, and this marked the
entrance to the old channel of the Euphrates, which
led by Kubaish down to Kurna. Once inside this
channel we had plenty of water, we got shelter
from the waves, and more important still, we had
got into a fair current, which became stronger as
we entered the river. The *mashufs*, now only two
miles behind, were still in the lake and not feeling
the current, so for a time we actually held our own
with them. Once inside the river, however, they
began to gain on us again, for the wind was strong
and they were being splendidly handled. But by

now we had rounded the last bend, and Kubaish was in sight only a mile away. The excitement amongst the officers had spread to the men, and all hands on both barges were anxiously watching the race. It seemed any odds now that we would be the winner, for we were almost at the post, unless the unexpected happened—and it did.

I wish to make it clear that what followed had nothing to do with me : the Arab skipper knew the channel and I didn't, so although I was on the bridge I was merely a spectator. He explained to me that just above Kubaish, although the river seemed broad and easy, in reality the channel became very narrow. On one side was a shoal which was steep-to ; on the other a long spit which he believed to be extending. Whether to avoid the latter he hugged the shoal too closely, I cannot say, but suddenly, in the language of river naviga- tion, we " shied off the shoal," swerved right across the river, and before we could do anything had brought up with a bump on the spit.

" Stout fellow," roared the sapper major exult- antly, while an exclamation of disappointment came from almost every one else on board.

Worse, however, was to follow. So severe was the bump that the lashings which made our barge fast to the stern-wheeler parted, and the barge could not, of course, be backed off until they were renewed. Before this could be done the first of the *mashufs*, full of excited, merry, cheering Gurkhas, and a couple of jeering officers, surged past, and before we got the barge clear of the spit the last of them had tied up to the bank at Kubaish.

The sun was almost setting when we eventually tied up just above the large paddler which was to embark the Gurkhas and also tow us to Kurna. As the skipper rang off the engines I descended from the stern-wheeler's bridge and clambered on to my own barge. I was weary and limp, for it had been a long hot day, and my eyes ached with the glare. I wore no coat, but my shirt, although dry, was white with the salt of perspiration, and my parched throat felt as if it were made of sandpaper. Moreover I knew that, with one exception, I hadn't at the moment a single friend on the barge. Here, however, I brightened up, the one exception was an important one—he was the only officer on the barge who had a supply of soda-water, and this he kept cool in a *coogee*, a porous vessel filled with water, on the fore-deck.

" Come along and have a drink," shouted the sapper major as soon as I appeared.

I am not in complete agreement with those who maintain that it is the sunset drink alone that makes life endurable in certain hot countries, but I certainly look upon it as one of the chief compensations. Wearily I dropped into one of the major's camp-chairs alongside his small collapsible table.

" Come and watch the chief conspirator receiving the reward for his dirty work," grunted one gunner officer darkly to another.

I heeded them not ; life at the moment was full of blissful anticipation—the soda-water was bubbling into the glass.

THE CASE OF THE *DILKHUSHA*.

I.

CAPTAIN JOE GREVILLE of the R.M.S. *Malabar* was on his last voyage up the river prior to proceeding on leave, and he was very glad indeed that it was so. He had been continually at work for the past four years, and was longing for a sight of England again and for the companionship of his wife and family.

The *Malabar* was a fine luxurious paddle-steamer over three hundred feet in length, well known with her various sisters to droves of tourists —the majority of them American—who patronised the country during the cold weather; and from the seaport which was her headquarters she penetrated over five hundred miles up an Eastern river, her terminus being the ancient capital of the country.

The river has two distinct personalities—high river and low river, the latter being naturally the more trying to navigators. During the dry season from November until March some of the navigable channels of the river, for all its length and apparent breadth and grandeur, become little more than ditches, so that a vessel such as the *Malabar*— which at that period had her draft limited to three feet six inches, and carried the bulk of her cargo in two flats, one lashed on each side—had at times considerable difficulty in getting through them. Indeed on occasion so shoal did the water become that when proceeding up-stream her commander had to run out a kedge anchor to help her across a bar ; then with engines going full speed ahead the chain which connected her bow with the kedge anchor would be hove round the windlass until gradually the vessel would slide over the shoal and reach the deeper water beyond. Coming down-stream such channels required different and even more careful treatment, for to steam down a narrow crooked channel with a strong current sweeping the vessel on would be to court disaster. Frequently the steamer had to be rounded-to above the channel, and the flats cast adrift and one by one carefully slacked down the stream until they reached the deeper and slacker water below. The steamer herself would then be backed down the channel, the flats brought alongside and lashed up again, and the whole outfit would turn round and continue the voyage down-stream with the prospect of repeating the performance at the next bad channel which they came to. For hundreds of miles during the low-water season, shoals, sand-banks, and even rocks would make navigation tedious and life to the navigator a burden.

The first rise in the river comes about March, and is due to the melting of the snows in the mountains far away to the north and east. Then follows the rainy season of the monsoon, and before long the river is in full flood—a mighty stream resembling in places an inland sea. Under those conditions, vessels like the *Malabar*, now loaded down to their full five feet draft, would steam triumphantly over shoals which a few weeks before had been standing out of the river high and dry like the roofs of houses, and would go alongside of previously deserted *ghauts*, which had been isolated half a mile from the water for months. High river, however, had also its dangers. Frequently blinding rain squalls would sweep across the face of the water, which was often covered with snags, drifting stumps, and, what was worst of all, large, low-lying, unmanageable rafts of teak-wood logs, which at times could only be distinguished by the fact that they had a small raised wooden hut, a flagstaff, and four or five men on board. One of those sighted close ahead when bowling down the centre of the stream during heavy rain would set the telegraph bells ringing and the engines racing full speed astern ; for when one's vessel is built for lightness and has plates of steel only an eighth of an inch thick, one doesn't hit anything, especially a solid log raft, if one can help it.

In view of the various emergencies which he was continually called upon to face, it is not surprising that although Joe Greville loved his work, and in fact had no desire for any other, four years of it were beginning to tell even on his robust constitution, and he felt badly the need for a change. His eyes were puckered and slightly bloodshot with peering into the intense glare, which would often cause the surface of the water to dance like a mirage in front of him as he tried to pick up the painted bamboos which served as buoys to mark a channel, or with trying to read the swirling water for signs of sand-banks or hidden snags. On this particular trip he was feeling nervous and jumpy. It wasn't that he knew anything of indecision or self-mistrust— there wasn't a more confident skipper on the river,—but his passage was booked on the first homeward-bound mail steamer which was due to leave the seaport after his arrival back, and he somehow feared that something would come in the way to stop his leave at the last moment. He remembered that on the two previous occasions on which he had gone on leave he had experienced the same jumpy feeling just beforehand, only not quite so bad, and he sometimes wondered if other men felt the same. He had no means of knowing—it is not the sort of thing that men discuss. One morning he addressed the mirror in his cabin which reflected his open, clean-shaven, still boyish face.

" Joe, old man," he said, " you're losing your dash."

Perhaps he was ; for after a man attains the age of fifty the navigating of a tropical river, with the long spells of duty, the night running, causing much broken rest, and the constant strain of his work—work which as a younger man he would have revelled in—becomes more and more a burden to him.

The *Malabar* duly arrived at her terminal port

up-country, and after a stay there of three days proceeded down-stream again. On the way down Greville received ample proof of his popularity on the river. At every station at which he tied up for a night, invitations to dine came on board, and at the funny little station clubs, to reach which he had to wade ankle-deep in dust, for it was now April and nearing the end of the dry season, he would find men who had ridden in some distance to have a final drink with him and to wish him a good leave. The river had already risen a bit, so he was single-handed that trip, had no flats in tow, and made good progress down-stream. He had no first-class passengers on board; the beginning of the hot weather had chased the tourists away, and few officials seemed to be travelling. The upper deck, which ran from the saloon, which was forward, clear to the stern, was, however, packed with native passengers, with their bundles, their food, and their jars and pots; and the subdued hum of many voices came from underneath the awnings as the vessel sweltered down the river.

II.

Down at the delta the river splits into half a dozen mouths, each of which reaches the sea but none of which are navigable. Further to the east, however, runs the river, on the banks of which lies the seaport which was the headquarters of the *Malabar*, and this river is navigable by large sea-going vessels. Connecting it with the main river was a broad, deep, tidal creek, and into this creek the *Malabar* swung about three o'clock one morning. Just after she had passed the large clump of elephant grass standing about twelve feet high, which marks the entrance to the creek, she met a very heavy rain squall—the first rain which the country had experienced for nearly six months. It was one of the so-called mango showers, which help to moisten the parched soil before the real monsoon breaks. So heavy was the rain that the *Malabar's* engines were put to slow, and her steam whistle was soon raising echoes from the wooded banks. The squall passed as quickly as it came, the stars reappeared, and although the night was dark, the steep jungle-clad banks of the creek could be clearly seen on either side.

Hitherto the *Malabar* had been running downstream, but now she was met in the teeth by a six-knot spring-flood tide, with the result that she was soon hugging the port bank. To the blue-water seaman this would appear to be an unusual procedure, but the river has laws of its own, and one of those is that the vessel steaming against the current hugs whichever bank gives the slackest water—usually the concave one—while the vessel which is steaming with the current keeps in mid-stream, where she gets the full benefit of it. With the aid of her powerful searchlight, which was mounted forward on the upper deck, the *Malabar* was making good progress. She was navigated from the lower deck right forward, her wheel and engine-room telegraph being situated on a platform just abaft the windlass. All the company's vessels were fitted in that way, the idea being that the nearer the commander was to the actual surface of the water, the better he could judge his distance from any object. On the *Malabar's* platform that morning were the native pilot ; the *seacunny*, or helmsman ; the *puriwallah*, or look-out man ; and the telegraph-man. The captain sat on a chair on the port side of the platform, and the only light visible on that part of the lower deck was that shown by the telegraph. The two British deck officers were asleep in their beds. Ordinarily they kept no watch, but supervised the handling of cargo at the various stations and the internal economy of the vessel.

The searchlight was trimmed to show about four points on the port bow—that is, at an angle of forty-five degrees with the line of the keel; and for all the many years that he had used one, Greville never tired of it. Its ray produced a scene on the river bank comparable only to a brilliantly lighted stage behind the footlights of a darkened theatre. Without it the banks of the creek had a sombre sameness: thick unbroken jungle appeared to rise steep on either side. The ray, however, revealed—as it swept steadily along the bank—breaks in the jungle: little villages hidden amongst the trees; small pagodas, some aged and half concealed by moss, others newly whitewashed; and at intervals little fields upon which paddy had been grown during the last rains, each one surrounded by *bunds* and many of them lined by betel-nut palms. Occasionally amongst the jungle trees themselves one would appear with large splashes of blood-red blossom showing up against its dark-green foliage. Viewed from the darkened vessel it was an enchanting panorama which the great moving circle of light disclosed, and from the bank there came the odour of earth which had been newly rained upon after being long parched, and the sweet sickly smell from a tree which the natives declare blossoms three times before the real rains break.

Greville sat back in his chair and contentedly puffed at his cheroot. He had only forty odd miles to go before he reached his destination, and then his troubles would be over for another eight months; by the end of that time he hoped to be full of vim and ready to face anything. Also it should be all plain sailing now. The creek was easy to navigate, while the river which he was approaching, although difficult for heavy sea-going vessels, was nothing to him with his light-draft paddler. Occasionally in low tones he would caution the native pilot if he thought that the latter was getting too close to the bank, or check him for getting too far out into the current; otherwise there was almost a dead silence on the darkened platform as the paddles churned and the vessel clove her way through the dark waters of the creek.

Presently there appeared just round a bend the green side-light, with a white light above it, of a vessel in the middle of the creek coming the other way. When the lights came clear of the bend, Greville got his night-glasses on to them. He decided that they belonged to one of the small steamers, or large launches, which ply between the small stations on the delta, and which are commanded by natives; and thinking that it might be one which belonged to the company, he ordered the searchlight to be switched on to her for purposes of identification. In the rays of the searchlight he saw rather a curious sight—what appeared to be an oblong canvas tent shut all round, with a small black funnel protruding from the top of the continuous flat awning which formed the roof of the tent, and the low black line of a hull underneath. She wasn't one of the company's launches: she was native owned, and it struck Greville at once that the canvas screens which are fitted all round such vessels had been lowered down for protection during the previous rain squall and had never been rolled up again. The result

was that the launch was rushing almost blindly
before the current, and her helmsman, who at
the moment was probably having a wordy argument with some of the native passengers, was
simply trusting to chance. To any one who does
not know India, and the casual indifference to
taking precautions that characterises a certain
class of native, this would seem almost incredible.
Yet even the ordinary globe-trotter in India must
have been struck by the way a *gharry wallah* or
cab-driver will, when hailed, dash blindly across
the street quite oblivious of any other traffic ; or
when he has to turn his cab round, by the way
that he will wheel his shabby little pony away
from the kerb without a single glance behind him.

"No wonder my hair is turning grey when
there are swine like that on the river," murmured
Greville, nodding in the direction of the launch.
"That dusky criminal ought to be shot or hanged
forthwith."

The searchlight was switched back on to the
port bank, and the creek was dark again. Although
the launch was out in the middle of the creek and
heading to pass well clear, the skipper kept a
watchful eye upon her, and it was well that he
did so, for suddenly a third light, a red one, gleamed
alongside of the green ; then the green was shut
out, and only the red and white were visible.
The launch's helm had been ported, and she was
now making to pass across the *Malabar's* bow.

"Damn !" said Greville. "Hard-a-port. Stand
by the engines."

He had sprung to his feet and was watching

the launch anxiously. The answering bell from the engine-room clanged in reply to the stand-by signal. The vessel swung out into the current, bringing the launch on to her port bow, and, red light opposed to red, the vessels were again passing clear of each other. To indicate the course which he was taking, Greville blew a short blast on the steam whistle. This signal had an entirely different effect to what he expected, for again the launch's three lights appeared, then only the green and white. The launch's helm had been starboarded, and she was again heading across the *Malabar's* bow, this time in a different direction. A collision could not now be avoided; the launch was rushing to her doom, wantonly committing suicide. Still the violence of the impact could be modified, and Greville ordered the engines full speed astern. It was fortunate for the launch that the *Malabar* was a paddle steamer, for such vessels lose their way very quickly; had she been a screw steamer she would have run right over the top of the launch, and probably drowned every person on board. As it was, she crashed into the launch just abaft the latter's starboard beam. There followed a grinding sound as the *Malabar's* sharp steel stem crunched into the launch's thin steel plates, the noise of splintering wood and of rending canvas, and the agonised screaming of women and children. For a moment the launch seemed to heave herself up on the *Malabar's* bow, then the vessels slowly drew apart.

III.

Greville's first orders were to stop the engines and call all hands ; then he rushed forward, switched on the electric light which was used when heaving up the anchor to watch how the cable grew, and peered over the side. The two vessels were now about six feet apart, and neither had any way through the water. The launch had been brought up all standing by the collision, and her engines had also been stopped, but whether by the accident or by design Greville did not know. He could see that the launch was a screw one about eighty feet long, and he instantly detected a gash in her side from the rubbing strake which ran along her gunwale right down to the water's edge ; it was quite enough to sink her. He shouted to the telegraph-man to put the *Malabar's* engines slow ahead, and to the *seacunny* to starboard the helm a little ; and the steamer, forging ahead slowly, again got her stem inserted into the gash in the launch's side.

" Steady the helm," Greville shouted. " Dead slow ahead."

By this time he had been joined by the two deck officers, both clad in pyjamas. He ordered the second officer to lower the big boat aft, come up on the *Malabar's* port side, and try to get alongside the launch's stern. Then he explained to the chief that he intended to keep touch with the launch, try to keep her afloat, and gradually sheer her into the bank. Through the gap which one of the *Malabar's* stanchions had torn in the purdah or canvas screen of the launch, they could see people struggling on her deck.

" If only they would cut away that blasted purdah," Greville shouted, as he made his way to a position between the wheel and the telegraph, both of which required tending, " we could rescue them all this way. Anyhow, get as many of them out as you can."

Like all river steamers, the *Malabar* had very little freeboard, so that, low in the water as the launch was—and she was gradually getting lower, —getting from one vessel to the other presented no great difficulty. The first man to do it was an elderly, bearded, native seaman clad in a loose shirt and a *dhoti* and wearing a sailor's cap. He appeared to be thoroughly scared, for the instant that he reached the *Malabar's* deck he seemed to be imbued with the idea of getting as far away from the accident as possible, and darted off into the darkness. The next man to appear in the gap in the purdah was a Chinaman, bland and unruffled. Hanging on his left wrist was a leather bag, and firmly grasped in his right hand was a silver-mounted umbrella.

" Catchee umb'ella," he said politely to the chief officer, who was hanging over the rail.

With considerable agility he followed the umbrella, retrieved it, and also disappeared aft into
the gloom. Man after man, Chinese and native
passengers and lascars, struggled through the gap
in the purdah, and reached the safety of the
Malabar's deck, the while the latter was steadily
pushing the launch in toward the port bank,
upon which the searchlight was playing for the
purpose of finding the best place to beach her.
Then Greville, who from his post was also watching the efforts of his officer and men to haul the
unfortunate wretches on board, decided that there
was something wrong.

" Here, Weller," he shouted to the chief officer,
" there are women and kids aboard of that launch
—I heard them screaming, and it's about time
some of them appeared. Where the hell is the
serang of the damned thing ? Find *him* and get
him to do something."

But all the chief officer's shouts for the serang
of the launch produced no result ; no one knew
where he was. At last Greville found a lascar less
panic-stricken than the others, and from him learned
that the serang was on board the *Malabar*, and
that the scared-looking elderly seaman who had
been the first man to leave the launch which he
commanded was he.

" I'll go down into the launch myself, sir, and
see what I can do," Weller shouted.

" All right," replied Greville.

The chief officer threw his leg over the rail
preparatory to dropping from his own vessel to
the other, then gave a startled shout.

" Go astern for God's sake, sir ; she's sinking."

Greville ordered the engines astern, and the *Malabar* drew back just in time to avoid running over the top of the launch, whose deck was now under water. Slowly her upper works, the fabric of steel, wood, and canvas, settled down, the short black funnel being the last thing to disappear. The surface of the water ahead of the *Malabar* was empty. Off on the port bow was the second officer's boat ; it had only two survivors from the launch on board. Those had struggled underneath the purdah, had jumped overboard and been picked up. Greville backed the *Malabar* about a hundred yards down the creek, then slowly steamed up again, the powerful searchlight sweeping the surface of the water. Not a living thing was to be seen, so he determined to anchor and wait for daylight.

After anchoring he sent for the serang of the launch, and questioned him. The launch was native owned, and was named the *Dilkhusha*. The serang had by no means got over the shock of the collision ; he was still badly scared, trembling, and wholly unnerved. When asked how many passengers he had on board, he replied vaguely, " Hundreds," which answer gave Greville a momentary shock, for not more than thirty people had been rescued. Obviously, however, the serang was so badly shaken that he did not know what he was talking about, and in the middle of the conversation the bland Chinaman came along, still grasping his silver-mounted umbrella, and gave it as his opinion that there had never been more than forty-five people on board the launch, including the crew. Still this was bad enough, and there was good reason to believe that most of those who had been left on board imprisoned within the walls of the purdah were women and children. The engine-driver was also amongst the missing ; when last seen he had been doing a job in the engine-room. He had died at his post —probably because no one had taken the trouble to tell him that it was time that he left it. The *Malabar's* own deck passengers had given no trouble throughout. Away up on their deck they had been rather remote from the point of impact, and they had never seemed to take the slightest interest in the proceedings.

Presently the sky began to pale. It was a calm still morning, giving promise of a grilling hot day. A deep hush, which gave a haunting sense of loneliness and desolation, brooded over the creek. The dawn crept stealthily along its banks, and the distant stretches of it began to reveal themselves. The water, which was as smooth as glass, gave off little isolated wreaths of white mist ; there was not the faintest breath of air, not a leaf stirred on the jungle-clad banks. The sun rose, and for a few minutes the surface of the creek ahead of the *Malabar* glowed blood-red ; then it gradually turned to its usual tint of greyish-brown. Two or three naked native children, drawn from some hut away back from the bank by the strange spectacle of a large steamer anchored there, came down to the water's edge and squatted under a tamarisk tree.

It was drawing near to high water ; the flood
tide had eased, and was now of no greater force
than one knot. There was no sign of the *Dilkhusha*,
not even a ripple to show where she lay covered
by forty feet of muddy water. While the second
officer went out in the boat and buoyed the wreck
by means of a boat's anchor, a line, and a plank,
Greville and the chief officer scanned the banks
through their telescopes, in the hope that some one
from the launch might have managed to swim
ashore, but their search was fruitless. With a
heavy heart Greville ordered the anchor to be hove
up, and proceeded on his voyage.

IV.

Greville had to postpone his leave and cancel his passage, for he had to await the court of inquiry into the collision and subsequent loss of life. The *Malabar* had proceeded to the dockyard for the few necessary repairs—the damage which she had received had been very slight—and for her annual overhaul, and Greville had remained in charge of her. The postponement of his leave had been decidedly vexing, but he had no qualms whatever about the inquiry. He awaited the result of it with complete equanimity, for he knew that he had acted both before and after the collision in a seamanlike manner.

Amongst the European inhabitants of the port, interest in the collision had died down very quickly. People were shocked when they first heard the news, for fatal accidents on the river were rare, but by the time that the inquiry came round the tragedy had been almost forgotten, with the result that the police court where the inquiry was held, although thronged with members of the various native races, contained less than a dozen Europeans, and they were mostly connected with the company's steamers. The inquiry was held by a British magistrate—sallow-faced and tired-looking, for he had been long in the country,—and he was aided by two nautical assessors, both shipmasters, who were almost as sallow, for their work lay entirely in tropical waters, where they navigated their vessels from under double awnings. It was generally considered amongst the shipping people of the port that the *Dilkhusha* had a poor case.

Counsel for the owners and serang of that vessel was of a different opinion, and he stated it fluently. He was a small, sharp-faced, whity-brown coloured barrister of mixed parentage, who possessed a loud rasping voice, with which he was an adept at confusing and brow-beating hostile witnesses—especially if they were natives. His case was that the *Malabar* had caused the collision by continuously playing her searchlight on to the *Dilkhusha*, so that the serang and helmsman of that vessel had been so dazzled and bewildered that they were quite unable to see where they were steering. Even then there would have been no collision had the *Malabar* not deliberately left the bank which she was hugging, and ported right out into the middle of the stream.

Counsel for the *Malabar*, on the other hand, contended that that vessel's searchlight had only once been flashed on to the *Dilkhusha*, and that the collision had been caused by that launch first of all porting across the steamer's bow and afterwards starboarding back again. This reckless and erratic steering was, he alleged, due to the criminal negligence of the serang of the *Dilkhusha*, who had allowed his purdahs or canvas screens to remain down all round the vessel, so that the helmsman could have no idea as to where his launch was heading. Also if those purdahs had not been down every passenger from the *Dilkhusha* would have been saved, and the regrettable loss of fifteen lives would have been avoided. Finally, the *Malabar* only ported out into the middle of the stream when it became necessary to avoid collision when the launch first showed her red light as a result of porting *her* helm and heading across the steamer's bow.

Greville was the first witness, and the hearing of his evidence took up some considerable time. In the witness-box he was admirable; he answered the questions put to him by his own counsel with the confidence of a skilled seaman sure of his case, and opposing counsel in cross-examination could make no impression upon him. When he stepped down from the box on the conclusion of his evidence, it was felt by all the Europeans present that he had placed the owners of the *Malabar* and himself in an impregnable position. The evidence of the officers which followed had mainly to do with the lowering of the boat and the dispositions made for saving life, as neither of them had been on deck when the collision occurred. Then came the first surprise of the inquiry. The native pilot had disappeared; no one had been able to find him; and the *puri-wallah*, a thin jungly-looking youth, was the next witness. He stated through an interpreter that the *Dilkhusha's* purdahs could not have been down all round, because at different times when the *Malabar's* searchlight played upon her, he could distinctly see the helmsman of the launch at the wheel and the serang standing beside him. As the witness glibly reeled off his evidence, Greville could do nothing but sit back in his chair and gaze up at him in complete astonishment, and before another witness could be called the court adjourned for the day.

The news quickly spread through the port that night that the case of the *Dilkhusha* was not turning out to be such a simple one after all, and when the inquiry was resumed the next morning the court was packed with men of all classes and colours. The telegraph-man was the first witness called, and he corroborated what the *puri-wallah* had said, nor could counsel for the *Malabar* shake him. The *seacunny* who had been at the *Malabar's* wheel followed ; he was an honest fellow, and Greville listened to him hopefully. He commenced by giving it as his opinion that the purdahs of the launch had been down, and that certainly the steamer's searchlight had only been flashed upon her once. Then under a vehement cross-examination from opposing counsel, he became confused, broke down, and finally contradicted his previous statements. Before the triumphant whity-brown barrister had finished with him he did not know what he was saying, and as he stepped down from the witness-box, Greville's friends realised that he had done the captain's case more harm than either the *puri-wallah* or the telegraph-man who had preceded him had done.

The next man to go into the box was the serang of the *Dilkhusha*, no longer the panic-stricken

individual who had trembled on the deck of the
Malabar. He looked venerable, grave, and stately
as he strode into the court. He was now wearing
a brand-new blue uniform, and on his head was
a little, round, snow-white cap, with a black band
round it ; on his band in letters of gold was the
name of the vessel which was now lying at the
bottom of the creek. In deliberate tones he
described the accident, and how, dazzled by the
brilliant powerful searchlight of the *Malabar*, he
and his anxious helmsman had been blinded, bewildered, and rendered helpless. As regards the
purdahs, the starboard one had certainly been
lowered for the comfort of his passengers when
the rain squall struck them, for the rain was
blowing in from that side. Those on the port
side and forward, however, had been rolled up
before they left port, and had never been lowered
afterwards. In answer to cross-examination as to
whether he had been the first man to leave the
sinking launch, he faced the court with dignity
and said that he had. The deck of his launch
had been crowded with passengers bewildered and
frightened by the crash of the collision, not knowing what to do and awaiting a lead. He had
bravely given it to them, and had been the first
man to go through the gap in the purdah to show
them the way. He had not given orders to cut
away the purdah on the starboard side of the
launch because he feared that she might sink at
any moment. He admitted, but rather reluctantly,
that had the *Malabar* not got her stem into the
gap in the launch's side, the latter would prob-

ably have sunk like a stone immediately after the collision.

That was the only little bit of evidence that was given in favour of the captain of the *Malabar* that day. While the crowded listeners in the court sweltered and gasped in its stifling atmosphere, and the *punkahs* over the heads of the tired-looking magistrate and the nautical assessors faintly swayed and creaked, witness after witness from the *Dilkhusha*, passengers as well as members of the crew, went into the box and fully corroborated the evidence of the serang. The bland Chinaman made an impressive witness, and he entered into more detail than the others did. He distinctly remembered the purdahs being rolled up before the vessel sailed, and those on the port side and forward were never lowered down again ; and he had watched the *Malabar's* searchlight, and been dazzled by it right up to the moment of impact. He paid a tribute to the serang of the *Dilkhusha* for his courage and calmness under the very trying conditions, and when he descended from the witness-box there was an outburst of applause from the natives at the back of the court. This was quickly suppressed. Some scandalised court peons and a couple of native policemen hurried to the spot, and, seizing two perfectly innocent Madrassis, threw them out into the corridor.

Finally, the ship's officers were recalled. They were both of the opinion that all the launch's purdahs were down, but, when pressed, neither of them were prepared to swear to this. The chief officer from his position on the steamer's port

bow could not possibly see the fore part of the
Dilkhusha, and the second officer in the boat was
in an even worse position. Counsel for the *Dilkhusha* had conducted his case with extreme cunning, for when the evidence was concluded, that
of Greville stood out alone, entirely unsupported
by one single witness either from his own steamer
or from the launch. The day being a Friday, the
case was adjourned until the following Monday,
when the arguments of respective counsel would
be heard and a decision given.

When the court had cleared Greville sought his
counsel, but received very little consolation from
him.

" I am afraid that it is almost a hopeless case,
captain," the latter said. " The evidence against
you is absolutely overwhelming. Sorry, I must
rush off now and do some work. We must just
hope for the best. See you on Monday morning."

He dashed off to his office for a cup of tea preparatory to getting busy over another brief, and
Greville turned disconsolately into the corridor.

V.

" Very bad business, sir, very," said a voice at his elbow.

Greville turned round and found that the speaker was the *Malabar's* clerk. This gentleman had native blood in him to the extent of about four annas in the rupee. He had been born and brought up in the country, and understood most of the dialects which were spoken in it ; indeed, he had been able to follow every word of the inquiry, much of which had, of a necessity, to be conducted through the medium of interpreters. Moreover, he had usually a pretty useful knowledge of all the underground intrigues which were carried on in the port, and always had the latest bazaar gossip at his finger-ends. He had the loquacity possessed by most of his class, and was a tireless talker, but much that he had to say was often interesting.

" Very bad business, sir," he repeated.

" It's a hell of a bad business, *krani*," Greville replied. " I never heard such a lot of damned liars in my life. Why, even if the searchlight *had* been played on them, they would never have noticed it behind those screens. But I can't make out the business, can you ? "

" Oh yes, sir," replied the clerk, " it is easily understood, but unfortunately not quite so easy to checkmate. It is a great conspiracy, sir ; what you might term a ramp."

" Quite. I can understand the attitude of the launch's crew, but not of her passengers. Some of them may be ignorant, but others, like that blasted Chink, for instance, must know perfectly well that if they had been left to the men of the launch they would have had a poor show. If it hadn't been for my officers and myself, most of them would probably be at the bottom of the creek now."

" True, sir, true," replied the clerk. " Their ingratitude is base, but there is a reason for it all which I will divulge to you. I happen to know, sir, that the native fellow who owns *Dilkhusha* is most impecunious. If he loses this case, sir, he will have to adopt one of two courses—either he will go bankrupt, or he will abscond from the country. Now I also happen to know, sir, that all those native passengers assert that they have lost all their valuables, and it would appear that they all had large sums of money in their possession—much larger sums, sir, than ever *I* saw a deck passenger carrying. They can't hope, sir, to recover anything from that native fellow who owns *Dilkhusha*, but if the *Malabar* loses the case, well, sir, the company is rich and can afford to pay out lakhs of rupees. Hence, sir, the reason for the milk reposing within the kernel of the cocoanut."

" Yes, but our own men—that damned *puri-wallah*, for instance."

The clerk waved a thin hand airily. " Without doubt, sir, they lied like stinking flat-fish ; but for that there is also a reason—bribery ; they have been got at, sir. That native pilot was also got at ; he dare not go into the box and lie, so he went sick and departed to his home in the most remote part of the delta, where no one could serve a subpœna on him. The *puri-wallah* and telegraph-man, sir, will return to their homes with enough money to keep them in comfort for years."

" What about the *seacunny* ? " asked Greville. " He has been with me for years. Why did he let me down ? "

" I believe, sir, that the poor fellow meant to tell the truth ; but he was first of all flummoxed, sir, and then carried away, by tempestuous verbosity of opposing counsel."

" He'll be carried away by the ambulance if I get my hands on him," said Greville.

Steps echoed along the now empty corridor. An Englishman, a friend of Greville's, was approaching. As he got nearer they made way for him, and the skipper hailed him.

" Good-evening, Reece," he said.

Reece did not take the slightest notice. Staring straight in front of him, he passed along the corridor. The slight was probably unintentional ; indeed if Greville had only paused to think, he would have remembered that Reece was one of the most absent-minded of men. Coming as it did, however, when his nerves were jangled by the events of the day—a day when everything seemed to have conspired to present him to the

public in the rôle of a liar,—it had the same effect
as if he had been slashed across the face with a
whip. The blood rushed to his head, and his
face flushed to the roots of his greying hair.

" My God," he muttered to himself, " that
fellow cut me just now, because he thinks that I
invented that yarn about the purdahs—that I
have deliberately lied to save my skin."

He bade the clerk a curt good-night, called a
taxi, and drove down to the ship. While he was
having tea his bearer packed his suit-case, and
afterwards he departed for the week-end to a
destination known only to the chief officer. He
was determined that no other person would get
the chance to treat him as Reece had done.

In flying off like that, however, he did his many
friends an injustice ; for wherever the case was
discussed that night—and it was the principal
topic in messes, clubs, and hotels—some one would
be found to declare stoutly that, no matter what
the result of the inquiry might turn out to be, if
Joe Greville said that a thing was so, it *was* so.
He wasn't built any other way.

VI.

The Indian regiment which at that time was
stationed at the port was the 141st Khataks, and
between that regiment and Joe Greville a great
friendship existed. He was an honorary member
of their mess, and no one who entered its anteroom
could produce from the officers who were assembled
there such an unanimous and enthusiastic shout
of " *Qui hai* " directed toward the lair of the mess
servants as he could as soon as he appeared. This
friendship had commenced, indirectly, many years
before. When Greville had completed his apprenticeship in a sailing-ship he had been in Cape
Town. A desire to get away from the sea for a
little while, and to see life up-country, had seized
him, and he had enlisted as a trooper in a regiment
of irregular horse which was about to serve in the
first Matebele war. In the same section of his troop
there was a young fellow fresh from an English
public school, and the two lads quickly became
sworn friends. After the campaign was over they
separated : Greville went back to sea, the other
proceeded to Sandhurst, afterwards entered the
Indian Army, and now commanded the 141st.
But that was not the only claim that Greville

had on the regiment. A few years before this unfortunate business of the *Dilkhusha* there had been some trouble up-country, and the regiment had been strung out on detachment along the upper reaches of the river, where they lived in various degrees of discomfort. Greville at the time had been in command of a 'bazaar boat,' which used to bank in for the night at all sorts of odd little stations, and any officer of the 141st who happened to be in the vicinity could always depend upon at least four things aboard of his steamer—a hearty welcome, a cold drink, a hot bath, and an excellent dinner.

On this particular Friday the regiment was having a guest night. Greville was to be one of the diners, and the officers of the regiment, more especially the younger ones, had made up their minds that under the peculiar circumstances it was up to them to show old Joe that he was *the* guest of the evening. There was considerable disappointment, therefore, in the anteroom when, just before the bugle sounded for dinner, the mess secretary received a chit to the effect that Greville was exceedingly sorry that he could not be with them that evening. The colonel, who knew his man, felt rather uneasy, and his uneasiness was considerably increased when after orderly room the next morning he opened the local newspaper. It contained a full report of the inquiry, and it was very plain to the colonel that things were going very badly with his old friend. He was kept busy all day, but after tea he drove down to the club, searched the reading-room, the billiard-room, the cosy small bar where Greville was often to be found, and finally the large bar. There he saw one of his majors sitting at a small table with a bronzed stranger, evidently a seafarer.

" Good - evening, Hunter," the colonel said. " Have you seen anything of Greville ? "

" I haven't, sir, although I have been watching for him. He isn't in the club. Sit down and have a drink. This is Norwood. He was chief officer of a large liner when I saw him last, but is now by way of being a salvage expert. He has just come out from home, and completed a big job down in the Mergui Archipelago."

The colonel sat down at the table, and a drink was ordered for him.

" Norwood and I have just been discussing Greville's case, sir," said Hunter. " Every one seems to think that he is in for a bad time."

" I am afraid that is so, colonel," Norwood said. " I don't know much about this mud-punching business, but I have been speaking to a few sailormen about the port to-day, and most of them think that Greville's river certificate will be cancelled."

While the other two chatted, the colonel sat back in his chair and allowed his thoughts to wander. His old friend's river certificate might be cancelled ; that meant that he would be finished with the company after all those years of service. It also probably meant going back to sea, making a fresh start when over fifty as third mate of a tramp or of a native-owned steamer. And nothing could be done ! He commenced to listen to the conversation of the others. Norwood was talking of his experiences around Mergui. They had had a devil of a time down there; had lived aboard a pearling lugger for a month, and were nearly grilled alive every day. He was glad that it was all over, and would be happy when he was on his way back to England.

" In the meantime," said Hunter, " you will be enjoying these few days in civilisation."

" I am, to a certain extent," Norwood replied, " but I have my worries too. Unfortunately I have a couple of full-blooded he-men on my hands—my divers. They also are celebrating their return to civilisation, and their principal desire seems to be to break the place up. They are safely treed-up at the moment at the sergeants' mess of the British regiment at the barracks; they have some friends there who invited them to a whist drive and dance. I can't imagine those two baby ele-phants dancing, but assuredly they will be mopping beer. It won't do them any harm, of course, for they can shift gallons of it, but all the same I will have to be on hand about ten o'clock to see them safely back to their little beds in the hotel."

The colonel suddenly sat upright in his chair.

" Divers ! did you say ? " he exclaimed.

" Yes, colonel. Two little beauties."

" Have they got their gear with them ? "

" They have, colonel. It's safely stowed away at the Government dockyard, but quite handy. Why ? "

" Because," replied the colonel slowly, " I think I could find a little job for them that would keep

them out of mischief over the week-end, if they
would take it on."

" They will take on anything, colonel. That's
one good thing about them. What is it ? "

The colonel explained his idea. It was to send
the divers in a launch to the wreck of the *Dilkhusha*.
They could go down and examine her, and might
be able to do Greville a good turn even yet.

" They will do it like a shot if it can be arranged,"
said Norwood ; " and I'll be only too glad to go
with them."

" Splendid," said the colonel, rising to his feet.
" The first thing to do is to find Greville. Hunter,
you might tell the people in the mess that I won't
be in for dinner. Your friend and I will have a
spot of food somewhere when we have got the thing
fixed up."

As the colonel had said, the first thing to do was
to find Greville ; but where ? Obviously the best
thing to do was to visit his ship. They called a
taxi, and went off through the native quarter of the
port to the line of wharves where the company's
steamers lay. At one of those the *Malabar* was
reposing idly ; she had just come up from the
dockyard and was awaiting her turn to go on the
berth. In appearance she was pretty hopeless :
she looked deserted and dark except for a few
dim lights, one of which was at the bottom of
the gangway.

" We might as well go on board and try our
luck," the colonel suggested rather despairingly.

Their luck was in, however. As they neared the
foot of the gangway they saw the chief officer com-

ing down it. He was dressed in mufti, and was obviously on his way up to the town.

"Good-evening, Weller," said the colonel. "Is Captain Greville on board?"

"Good-evening, colonel," replied Weller. "I'm sorry he isn't."

"Do you know where he is?"

Weller hesitated. "Well, I do, colonel," he said doubtfully, "but I fancy that he doesn't want to see any one."

"I *must* see him," said the colonel firmly. "Tell me where he is, and I will take the responsibility of going to him."

"You would never find the place, colonel," Weller replied. "I'll have to go with you."

"Right," said the colonel; "jump into the taxi."

Under Weller's direction the taxi again passed through the native quarter, then through cantonments, and finally on to the main road up-country which lay beyond them. The rains had not yet broken, it was a stifling night, and the wind which the taxi made was burning hot. They were soon enveloped in clouds of dust, for the road was lined on both sides by jungle trees, and between those trees and the tar macadam were dusty paths, along which there proceeded two constant streams of bullock carts. Once the taxi-driver, amid a stream of profanity and a grinding of brakes, brought the taxi up all standing within three feet of a pair of bullocks. Those, entirely contrary to police regulations, were wandering placidly down the centre of the road, their driver fast asleep in the cart behind them.

As they sped along an idea as to their probable destination suddenly dawned upon the colonel, for he remembered a gentleman whom Greville variously described as his ' low-down pal,' or as his ' disreputable friend.' On being questioned by the colonel one day about this mysterious person, he had confessed that the ' disreputable friend's ' only crime against society was the fact that he loathed it. On three or four occasions during the year he most unwillingly dressed for dinner and attended an official function ; on every other day he hastened home from his office, got into comfortable, loose, native clothes, and either loafed about the jungle adjacent to his bungalow or lost himself amongst his books. In fact he was almost a recluse, and Greville was one of the very few white men who had visited his bungalow. What more natural than that the skipper had taken refuge there now ? The colonel did not anticipate that they would receive a very cordial welcome ; indeed, he felt that their visit would be rather embarrassing. But it is significant that he never doubted for a moment but that his old friend would seize this chance to clear himself. Norwood, on the other hand, felt rather pessimistic about the whole business as they bumped and swayed over the numerous pot-holes on the road, for the taxi-driver was a reckless youth and was apparently in a hurry. After all, the salvage expert thought, the evidence *was* rather overwhelming against Greville.

He wondered if they were on a wild-goose chase.

Presently Weller stopped the taxi at a gap in the trees. They got out, walked along a narrow lane bordered on both sides by a bamboo hedge, then came to a clearing, and the bungalow stood before them. Without doubt its occupants were at home, for two fiery cheroot ends gleamed on the low verandah, and before long, under a hanging lamp which was surrounded by a cloud of small green flies, they could distinguish two men. The 'disreputable friend' was lying back in a long chair, comfortably clad in a singlet and loose native sleeping-pants. Greville was, however, fully clothed except that he had taken off his tussore silk coat and rolled up his shirt sleeves. A horrified native servant tried to stop them as they ascended the few steps, but the colonel resolutely brushed him aside, and the party debouched on to the verandah, Weller unobtrusively bringing up the rear. Their appearance caused something akin to consternation. The 'disreputable friend' sprang from his chair and gazed at them in amazement. He quickly recovered, however.

" Friends of yours, Joe ? " he queried.

" Two of them are," replied Greville, who had not moved, but had remained in his chair glaring at the shrinking Weller.

" H'm ! Ask them to have a drink, then."

The colonel went over to the chair on which Greville was reclining.

" Well, old boy, this is a bad business of yours," he said. " What are you going to do about it ? "

"*Do* about it," Greville retorted bitterly. "What *can* I do about it? If they care to take the word of a lousy native who was the first man to clear out of his ship and leave a lot of women and kids to drown against mine, they can. I'm fed up and sick of the whole show."

"Easy on, Joe, old boy," said the colonel gently. "That sort of talk won't do any good, and what's more, you can't afford it. You know what this means to you better than I can tell you. I don't pretend to know much about your private affairs, of course, but — well, that boy at Sandhurst must be a bit of a financial drag to begin with."

Greville reflected for a moment. "You're quite right, Charles," he said simply. "I'm sorry. But, I repeat, what can I do?"

"Ah," said the colonel cheerfully, "that's what we've come about."

He proceeded to explain the purpose of their visit. Long before he had finished, Greville was on his feet listening intently, Norwood watching him closely the while.

"So we kept the taxi on, and it's waiting at the end of the lane," the colonel concluded. "What about it?"

"By heavens! Charles, what a chance," Greville burst out excitedly. "But look here, we haven't much time to waste. Round about low-water slack would be the best time to do the business—easier for the divers, and the water is clearer too. Low water down there would be about eight o'clock to-morrow morning."

A scarcely concealed sigh of relief escaped Norwood.

"Can you get a launch to take the divers and ourselves there, and to tow the diving boat?" he asked.

"Rather," Greville almost shouted as he pulled on his coat. "I'll get one from the manager of the company. He's as keen to clear up this business as I am. Come on."

VII.

On the following Monday the court was again crowded, its occupants drawn there more for the purpose of witnessing a poignant human drama than from any anxiety to learn the result of the inquiry, for to most people that result seemed to be in the nature of a foregone conclusion. From the very outset a surprise awaited those who attended the court, for instead of speeches from the opposing counsel, which they had expected, counsel for the *Malabar* put in a plea that fresh evidence which was very material, and which had only been acquired over the week-end, might be heard. Counsel for the *Dilkhusha* strongly objected, but the magistrate, after consulting with the nautical assessors, directed that such evidence should be heard.

Not only was the evidence new, but the men who were about to give it were of a different type to any that had previously been seen in that court, for in response to a summons from a court peon, there presently rolled in a burly bull-necked individual with huge shoulders and a large red face. Englishman was written all over him, and in his freshness he contrasted almost as strongly with his sun-dried fellow-countrymen as he did with the natives, yellow and brown, who thronged the court. No other country but England could have bred him; he actually conveyed the impression that his staple diet when there must be good English beef and beer. He solemnly mounted to the witness-box, took the oath, and then gazed with a tolerant curiosity round the court.

In reply to counsel for the *Malabar*, he described how he had visited the wreck of the *Dilkhusha* the previous morning. She had evidently gone down bodily, and being flat-bottomed, was standing upright. The bed of the creek was not too soft, and the vessel had settled down about six inches into the mud; he believed that if a simple patch were put on her side, the vacuum created by the mud could be easily broken, and raising her would present no difficulty. He and his mate had walked right round her. It had been rather difficult to see very far owing to the muddy nature of the water, but they had both seen and felt several corpses which were lying jammed inside the rails. A hush pervaded the court, broken only by the thin voice of counsel and the deep-toned replies of the witness. The listeners, especially those who understood English, hung upon the diver's words, and even those natives who could not understand him gazed at him as if they were fascinated. At last came the question—dry and deliberate—which every one who realised what the evidence was leading up to, eagerly awaited.

" Will you tell the court in what position you found the purdahs ? "

Seemingly rather perplexed, the diver stared at counsel.

" The *wot*-ahs ? " he asked.

The tension in court seemed to snap. Everybody grinned, with the exception of the whity-brown barrister ; even the tired-looking magistrate smiled behind his hand. For the first time he was beginning to enjoy this case, for this witness with his simple directness and his homely Kentish accent seemed to him to have brought a breath of the fresh east wind which swirls around the South Foreland in the spring into the jaded atmosphere of the court ; and the court felt all the better for it.

" I mean the canvas screens which in such vessels are lowered down at times to protect the passengers and crew from rain or sun," said counsel.

" Them screens was down," witness replied.

" Do you mean down all round the vessel ? " one of the nautical assessors asked.

" Yes, down all round the vessel, sir," the diver replied smartly. He evidently realised that he was addressing an officer of the nautical profession. " There wos a tear in one of 'em on the starboard side from the awnin' spar right down to the rail, but apart from that, when we wanted to see on to the vessel's deck me an' my mate 'ad to bend down an' peer through between the rails."

Counsel for the *Malabar* sat down, and the whity-brown barrister arose to take up the running. He was cunning enough to realise that ' tempestuous verbosity ' was an utterly useless weapon against this solid phlegmatic Englishman, so he screwed his face into the nearest approach to a smile which he could contrive, and commenced suggestively.

"Would it surprise you to learn that a dozen witnesses in this court have sworn on oath that the screens on the port side of the vessel and forward were rolled up at the commencement of the voyage and never lowered down again ? " he asked.

The witness shook his head solemnly.

"No," he replied.

He somehow contrived to give the impression that nothing that had been sworn in that court would surprise him. The tired-looking magistrate again smiled : most of his days were spent in un-ravelling tangled skeins of lies woven by plausible witnesses in various alien languages, and the diver with his transparent bluntness was certainly the most refreshing witness that had been in his court for a long time.

"And I suggest to you," continued the whity-brown barrister, "that if those screens were in the position which you describe, they must have been washed down by the action of the current."

The diver raised a ham-like paw and with a thick forefinger reflectively scratched the top of his head.

"Well, so far as *I* know," he replied with a glance at the magistrate, "there ain't no 'arm in you suggestin' anything, only yer suggestion 'appens to be wrong. Them screens was not only down all round the vessel, but they was *lashed* down, with 'arf inch point-line stops each one about a fathom apart. An' no action of the current as ever I 'eard of could take a round turn with a point-line stop around an iron rail an' finish up with two 'arf 'itches around its own part. No ! No action of the current as ever I 'eard of could do that."

Ten days later—just about the time that the native fellow who owned *Dilkhusha* was absconding from the country—Joe Greville was pacing the saloon deck of a large passenger liner sailing over blue water—homeward-bound, without a care in the world.

THE TIMBER DROGHER.

I.

IT happened about a year before I finally 'swallowed the anchor.' I was still quite a youngster, only a few months out of sail, and was fourth officer of a large 'bull-boat' which belonged to a Scottish firm, and ran between various ports in Eastern Canada and the east coast of Scotland. I remember that it was our last voyage from Montreal for the season, for the ice would have closed the St Lawrence before we got back. For some reason we had no cattle on board that trip, with the effect that, with all the weight of her cargo below, she was pretty stiff and inclined to roll heavily. We had experienced a south-west gale and thick weather all the way from Cape Race, with the result that we had had few opportunities to get decent observation. The wind had, however, gone round to the north-west during the night, and it was clearing up, but there was a heavy sea rolling up on the port quarter which caused the old boat to lurch about a good deal. We had still another day to put in on the open ocean, but expected to sight the group-flashing light on Flannan Island, or the Butt of Lewis, early the next morning prior to proceeding through the Pentland Firth.

I was on watch with the chief officer from 4 A.M. until eight, and about half-past five daylight came in and revealed a most uninteresting sight. From the high bridge to the horizon on all sides there was nothing to be seen but a grey waste of white-capped ridges. It was bitterly cold too. Presently the officers' steward, a hospitable lad and a very welcome visitor at that moment, came up the bridge ladder on the starboard side and made his way across to the weather side, where, under the lee of the dodger, he let down a temporary table which had been stopped up to the rails. He then left the bridge, but à few minutes later reappeared, this time carrying a tray, on which there was a large pile of hot buttered toast, a big jug of coffee, and two mugs. We got grand coffee on that ship. I was standing beside the binnacle when the steward passed me on his way to windward and got a whiff of it. By Jove ! the smell was fragrant. The chief officer was already sheltering behind the dodger, and after a good look round I joined him, smacking my lips in anticipation. The steward paused for a moment, gazing forward over the top of the dodger before going below again. Suddenly he pointed over the bow and ejaculated—

"Good God, sir ! what's that ? "

Considerably startled, the chief and I left our coffee and gazed toward where he was pointing, but for a moment we could see nothing. Then just as a shout of " Broken water right ahead " came from the look-out man up in the crow's-nest, we picked up something. It was a black irregular-shaped object less than half a mile ahead. The same idea struck the chief officer that struck me, for we exclaimed simultaneously—

" Rockall ! "

That rock which rears its head seventy feet out of the Atlantic lies about 260 miles to the westward of the Outer Hebrides. It stands almost in the centre of a large bank which runs roughly north and south, and is about sixty miles long by thirty-five miles wide. Close to the rock there is a depth of about forty-two fathoms, and the average depth over the whole of the bank would be about seventy-five. All round it is much deeper water, averaging hundreds of fathoms. The great circle track which we were following runs from a position due east of Cape Race to the Butt of Lewis, and passes thirty miles north of the rock itself, so apparently we had got well off our course. The chief officer ordered the quartermaster at the wheel to port a couple of points, then he addressed me—

" By heavens ! " he said, " it's a blessing that it's daylight. How could we have got so far to the south'ard ? Call the old man and tell him that we sighted Rockall dead ahead, and that I am passing to the south of it."

As I went off the bridge to go to the captain's cabin, which lay beneath it, I also was wondering how we could have got so far off our course. I remembered reading on the chart the evening before that " an area of magnetic disturbance is reported to exist two to three miles to the N. and N.E. of Rockall," but I could not imagine that our compasses could have been affected to the extent of taking us thirty miles off our course. The captain's cabin was dark, the door was shut, and the curtains of every port drawn. He was a man who really loved his bunk. When we were in open water, clear of the land, he would go to it about 9 P.M., and it would take something decidedly serious to get him out of it before eight o'clock the next morning. I switched on one of the electric lights in his cabin, woke him up, and gave him the chief officer's message. He yawned and stretched himself, then answered me.

" Rockall right ahead, did you say ? How the devil did it manage to get there ? Right, tell the chief officer to pass to the south of it. It's steep-to, but don't run it too fine. He'll want to lay off a new course for the Butt of Lewis, too, and you had better get an azimuth as soon as you can and see what the error of the compass is."

With that the old man turned over, and, feeling myself dismissed, I left his cabin and regained the bridge. The chief officer was gazing through his binoculars out on the port bow. I got hold of mine, after giving him the captain's orders, and did the same.

" That's not Rockall," he exclaimed presently ; " it's a large piece of wreckage—quite big enough to damage a ship all the same. Better call the old man again, and tell him about it."

I sought the captain's cabin, and once more he yawned and stretched.

" All right," he replied patiently in answer to my information. " Tell the chief officer to get a

a very heavy sea running, mister," he pronounced gravely. " I don't know if I can risk lowering a boat. Could we get volunteers, do you think ? "

I stepped up to where he stood beside the wheel.

" I'll go for one, sir," I said eagerly.

" You would," he replied. " You haven't got the sense to know any better."

I fell back rather abashed. The vessel was now beam on to the sea and rolling very heavily. The captain called me to him again.

" Look here, Norris," he said kindly, " there's a heavy sea running, isn't there ? "

" Yes, sir," I replied.

" Yes, even from this high bridge it looks heavy, doesn't it ? Well, let me tell you that from a boat it will look twice as high—in fact it will look terrifying. Now do you still want to go ? "

I realised that I had spoken out of my turn, but felt that I couldn't draw back then—not if the sea was as high as St Paul's.

" Yes, I'll go, sir," I said.

" Well," he replied slowly, " if you can get two men to go with you—they must be volunteers, remember—you can go."

" Two men, sir," I said in surprise.

" Yes, two," he replied sharply. " That will be quite enough the way that I'll work it. You had better hurry up and try to get them while I manoeuvre to get to windward of the wreck."

He staggered across to the port side of the bridge. The steamer, with her helm hard a-starboard, was swinging up into the wind. I was making for the bridge ladder on the starboard side on my way down to the next deck in quest of volunteers, when the quartermaster at the wheel spoke to me.

" Sir," he said, " I'll be one o' them."

The quartermaster was a tall, dark, powerfully built man of a saturnine nature, named Malone. He hailed from County Cork, and I strongly suspected him of having Fenian tendencies. Apart from giving him helm orders, I had hardly spoken two words to him the whole voyage, but in some subtle way he had managed to convey to me the impression that there were two impediments in the way of my being a good officer—I was too young and I was an Englishman.

" An' there's another, sir," he continued ; " ask him."

A young able seaman named Driscoll had just come up on the bridge to do some job ; he was carrying a bucket of water and a swab. He was, I imagine, a ' townee ' of Malone's. He was a much smaller man than the quartermaster, and I looked at him doubtfully.

" He'll do, sir," urged Malone ; " sure he has the guts."

I approached Driscoll, told him what we proposed to do, and said that, of course, he was quite free to decline, as it was a volunteer that I wanted. He never even troubled to look at the sea or the wreck.

" If it's good enough for you an' Malone, sir," he said indifferently, " well, it's good enough for me."

I sought the captain, who, having steadied the steamer head to wind and put the engines to slow, was now in the chart-room, and told him that I had secured my two volunteers.

" You've been damned smart about it," he said. " Who are they ? "

" Malone and Driscoll, sir."

" Splendid," the captain replied cheerfully ; " you couldn't have done better. Malone is as strong as a dray-horse, and Driscoll is as active as a kitten. Get another quartermaster to relieve the wheel, then bring the two of them in here."

When we were gathered in the chart-room the captain explained his plan, and we learned why only three of us were going in a lifeboat, which ordinarily would require at least double the number. He was going to place the steamer to windward of the wreck, and slack the boat down to it by means of a long line. When we had rescued who-ever was on the wreckage, he would then heave the boat back to the steamer, drifting down toward it the while. We would thus not be required to use oars at all, with the exception of one, and in that one there lay a bit of a snag.

" Can you use a steering oar ? " he asked me suddenly. " A rudder is useless for keeping a life-boat head to sea when she has no headway on her."

That would have stumped a good many deep-water seamen, but fortunately I had had a good deal of experience with a steering oar in Western Australia, where we had to bring off a lot of the cargo through the surf in our own boats—and I was able to assure him that I could use one.

" Good," he said. " Now the whole thing de-pends on a small code of signals. Malone, who will be in the bow of the boat, will make them, but you have all got to know them in case of—well, you never know what may happen."

The code was simple. If we wished the line slacked away on board, Malone would stretch out his right arm horizontally ; if we wished the line hove in, he would stretch his left arm in the same way ; when we wanted the line held on, he would raise one of his arms above his head. An officer would be stationed at the taffrail aft with his glasses glued on the boat. The captain made us repeat the code until he was certain that we knew it ; then we went out on to the bridge. All hands had in the meantime been called. The third officer was on the bridge standing by the telegraph and watching the steering ; the second, with one watch, was swinging out one of the lifeboats on the starboard side ; while the chief had got up from the fore-peak a coil of new 3½-inch Manilla rope, and was stretching it along the deck. We put on lifebelts, then made our way along to the boat, which was now swung out, and got into her. The end of the Manilla rope had been rove through the ring-bolt in the bow of the boat, a few fathoms of it had been hauled through, and the bight of it had been hitched round one of the forward thwarts. A new heaving line and a life-buoy had been placed in the boat, and all the oars save two had been taken out. The steamer being now to windward of the wreckage, her head was canted to starboard so as to make a lee for the boat on that side, and the engines stopped. It was still blowing hard from the nor'-west—a keen, clear, cutting wind.

" Lower away."

The order came through a megaphone from the bridge. While one of the hands forward poured oil from a five-gallon drum into the sea, the boat slid slowly down the side into a comparative calm. A wave, its crest smoothed by the oil, rose up to meet her and, water-borne, she subsided with it. The davit-fall blocks were unhooked, and save for the Manilla rope we were free from the ship. I shipped the steering oar. The steamer's engines were put ahead again, and rising and falling with the swell the boat slowly drifted aft.

II.

Still sheltered from the weather by the protecting wall of the steamer's hull, we passed aft under her counter, and in another moment we were clear. Then we got it. A huge wave came surging past the steamer's stern, caught hold of the boat, and seemed to throw her yards upwards. As we perched dizzily on its crest, the flying spray lashed me across the face like a whip, and for the moment blinded me, then the boat seemed to fall like a stone, and I felt as if the pit of my stomach had dropped out. The Manilla rope tightened with a jerk, and the boat surged up as the crest of the next wave rushed at her. Almost stunned by the force of the wind, the driving spray, and the tremendous surge of the waves, I struggled with the steering oar to keep the boat head on to the sea. As the captain had predicted, the sea looked terrifying, and for a moment I *was* almost terrified ; certainly I was completely confused. I didn't think just then that the boat could possibly live. I got my eyes clear of water, collected my thoughts, and took stock of my companions. Malone stood upright in the bows, a leg on each side of the forward thwart, which he was gripping with his knees. Occasionally he stretched out his right arm hori-

zontally as if to show that we still required the line
to be slacked away, the action, I expect, being sub-
conscious, for the officer at the steamer's taffrail
could see that we were still some distance off the
wreck.   Driscoll, crouching in the bottom of the
boat, was hitching the bight of the heaving line to
the life-buoy, and when he had completed that he
made one end of the line fast round his waist and
the other end fast to a thwart.

The most sickening feeling of all was when we
dropped down into the trough between the waves,
where we could see nothing but a wall of water
ahead of us and another wall behind.   I soon
noticed, however, that when the boat was in that
position I could recover my breath, and as I got
more used to the thing I grasped the opportunity
when up on the crest of a wave to notice the relative
positions of the steamer and the wreckage.   The
former had been beautifully handled, and was now
head to wind, with the boat-rope with which we
were being slacked down leading over her stern,
and she was dead to windward of the wreck.   All
that I had to do was to keep the boat head on to
the sea, and give the order to hold on the line when
she had been slacked down far enough.   Some one
had been pouring oil copiously over the steamer's
stern, and the crests of the waves were, in consequence, becoming rather smoother.   Occasionally,
in an endeavour to judge the distance we were still
off the wreckage, I would glance over my shoulder.
Not a word had been spoken in the boat since we
had left the steamer until suddenly Driscoll, who
was facing aft, shouted—

" Look out, sir. We're on top o' the wreck."

Considerably startled, for I thought that we were still some distance off, I looked round, to see the ragged stump of a mast with the fife-rail attached and several belaying-pins sticking out from it like teeth, almost level with the water, and only about ten feet off the boat's port quarter. Somehow or other I had formed the opinion that the wreckage, about twenty feet long, which we had sighted from the steamer was only a part of a vessel, and I had imagined vaguely that she might have been cut in two by some fast liner, and that the after part had been left floating. Now, however, I realised that the whole ship was here, and that her bow must be floating about thirty feet below the mean level of the waves. Her deck was like a sloping beach, up which the waves were rushing and frothing, high-water mark being represented by the small part of the vessel which was showing above the sea. Other things were now occasionally visible upon the deck —the stump of another mast and the iron wheels of the pumps. With a wrench of the steering oar I sheered the boat off to starboard just in time to avoid having her stove in on the deck of the derelict. We were soon close enough for our purpose.

" Hold on, Malone," I shouted.

Malone's right hand shot straight up above his head ; the boat-rope tightened up, and we were, as I thought, in a good position just slightly to wind-ward of the wreckage. The dog still lay across the after part of the skylight ; the man—an old chap, bareheaded, with white whiskers, evidently very exhausted and thoroughly soaked—was lashed to a

ring-bolt alongside the bulwark on the port side,
the yellow-white of the rope lashing round his waist
showing vividly against his tattered black oilskin
coat. Besides being down by the head the derelict
was listed to starboard heavily, which was the
reason why I had chosen to go on that side, and in
some mysterious way, although continually rising
and falling, she was lying head on to the wind and
sea. To my horror the boat, instead of remaining
in position, was drifting rapidly past the wreck—
evidently I hadn't been quick enough in ordering
Malone to signal to hold on the line. I declare that
I could feel myself blushing with shame. What an
incompetent ass they must all be thinking me!
the captain of our steamer, whose binoculars would
be fixed on the boat, the boat's crew, even the old
chap whom we were trying to rescue. He, poor
old fellow, was apparently trying to tell me something as we surged past, but, although his lips
moved, no sound came from them ; with his right
hand, which still held the handkerchief with which
he had been waving to us, he was pointing toward
the position of the submerged bow. There was
nothing for it but to get to windward again.

" Heave in, Malone," I ordered.

Malone's left arm was extended horizontally, and
the boat began to creep to windward over the
crests and down into the hollows, until we were
again a little bit ahead of where the old man was
lying. I told Malone to signal to hold on and Driscoll to get ready, but again the boat began to surge
to leeward past the wreck. The old man was now
trying harder than ever to draw my attention to

something forward. Suddenly, without any fresh orders from me, the boat-rope tightened up again ; the boat got into position, and was held there, as I afterwards learned, by the steamer's engines being kept turning slowly ahead. The captain had divined our difficulty.

I was now to learn why it was well that Driscoll was as active as a kitten. I sheered the boat as near to the wreck as I could safely go, then, first balancing for an instant on the boat's gunwale, the able seaman made a flying leap and landed on the sloping deck of the derelict. Desperately struggling to hold on, he was sliding back into the sea when a wave came along and washed him almost up to where the old man lay along the bulwark, quite unable to help him. Driscoll grabbed the lashing which was round him, manœuvred himself into a position with his feet between the bulwark and the old chap's body, and then commenced by means of the heaving line to haul toward him the life-buoy which Malone had just dropped overboard. He slipped the buoy round the old man's feet, and gradually worked it up toward his waist, then drew his sheath-knife, severed the lashing, and worked the buoy up under the old man's armpits.

" Haul away, Malone," he yelled.

While Driscoll was cutting the lashing I had ordered the boat to be slacked down a bit, so that she was now to leeward, and it was an easy matter for Malone to haul the old chap off the sloping deck of the derelict into the water and alongside the boat. Then it became evident to me why it was necessary that Malone should be as strong as a dray-horse—he had to get the rescued man into the boat. Leaning over the gunwale he got both hands under the life-buoy, and with a tremendous heave he raised the old man right out of the water and deposited him, as tenderly as if he were a child, in the bottom of the boat. Again Malone leant over the gunwale, and for the first time since we left the steamer he spoke—

" Come away thin, owld fella me lad," he said.

I looked over the side. The dog, swimming strongly, was making for the boat, his handsome yellow head—he was a golden retriever—steering straight for Malone. The quartermaster laid hold of him well up on the fore-legs ; there was another heave, and the heavy animal was deposited in the boat as tenderly as his master had been. The dog licked the old man's face, and was rewarded by a feeble pat ; then the two lay very still on the bottom boards between the thwarts. We had now to recover Driscoll, but that was easy. The end of the heaving line was still fast round his waist ; he plunged into the sea, and Malone soon hauled him alongside and lifted him into the boat.

" Right," I shouted to Malone as I sheered the boat away from the wreck ; " heave in."

From the crest of each successive wave which we climbed I watched the steamer. Her helm had evidently been put hard a-port, for her head gradually fell off in our direction until she was lying beam on to the seas. The lead for the boat-rope had also been shifted—it was now rove through one of the mooring ports amidships. Very slowly they hove in on it ; indeed I fancy that they only took in the

slack as the steamer drifted down toward us. The
sea grew calmer as we drew under her lee, and before
long we were rising and falling on the well-oiled
waves against her rusty side. The blocks of the
davit-tackle falls were hooked on, and the boat
hoisted up level with her rail ; the old man and the
dog were lifted out, and I can assure you that I
breathed a silent prayer of thankfulness as I stepped
once more on to the steamer's deck.

"Go below and get into dry clothes, you men,"
the captain shouted from the bridge.

It was a very welcome order, for we were all
soaked to the skin, and now that the excitement
was over I was shivering in the cutting wind. I
went to my cabin, smoked a cigarette while I
changed, and returned to the bridge. Quick as I
thought I had been, Malone was before me. When
I reached the bridge his hands were gripping the
spokes of the wheel, and his eyes were glued on the
compass card.

III.

Two days afterwards in the late afternoon we arrived at our port, and when we were fast alongside the quay wall and the work was over, I sought my cabin. The chief officer's wife, who had arrived from her home by train, had been waiting on the quay, and was now on board ; that meant that he would keep ship that evening and that we juniors would be free. I was thinking of visiting the third officer, who lived in the next cabin, to propose an excursion up-town in search of a theatre with a decent show in it, when there was a knock on my door. I opened it, and found Malone standing in the alley-way.

" The owld fella from the wreck would like to see ye, sir," he said.

It was the first chance that I had had to speak to Malone since the rescue, and I thought it a fitting time to thank him for having gone in the boat with me. I tried to improve the occasion by a modest reference to our comrades in distress and the brotherhood of the sea, and thought that I had made quite a nice little speech. Malone listened in silence until I had finished.

" Ah, not another word, Mr Norris," he said.

"If I can say so without givin' ye offence, sir, ye handled that boat well—far better than ever I expected ye would do. But when it comes to the brotherhood of the sea, sir—there's no such thing ever existed betwixt me an' annythin' that ever sailed out o' Belfast."

"But," I exclaimed in astonishment, "you knew that the wreck belonged to Belfast before you volunteered to go in the boat."

"'Tis true, sir, I did," he replied with dignity, "but I wouldn't have it on me conscience that I'd left a dog to dhrown."

That finished *me*. I proceeded along to the saloon to visit the "owld fella from the wreck." Incidentally I had discovered that she had been a timber-laden brig, and that the "owld fella" had been the master of her. I knocked at the door of the stateroom in which he had been put to bed, with hot bottles all round him and a stiff peg of brandy inside after a hot bath. He shouted to me to enter. I opened the door and found him sitting up on a settee fully clad in some clothes that our old man had given him. The dog was lying on the floor at his feet, its head resting on its paws ; its tail flapped once or twice in welcome as I entered. Both of them were looking less the worse for wear than they did when I had seen them last. The dog had also had a hot bath, and he had been groomed—it didn't surprise me to hear that Malone had been looking after him,—and the old man in his borrowed clothes looked quite smart, although still rather exhausted.

"Good-evening, Mr Norris. Please sit down," he said.

I opened out a camp-stool which was part of the furniture of the stateroom, and sat down beside him.

"I didn't send for you to thank you for what you did for me, for I know that you don't want thanks," the old man said, "but I wished to explain something which I could see was worrying you at the time and probably still is, for I imagine that you are a keen young officer. It wasn't your fault that you twice drifted past the brig with your boat, for both the boat and the steamer were drifting to leeward, whereas the brig was stationary. She was anchored, as I tried to tell you at the time."

"Anchored!" I exclaimed. "How could she be anchored in the middle of the ocean?"

The old man smiled. "She *was* in the middle of the ocean," he replied, "but she was anchored all the same. She was on the northern edge of Rockall Bank. Your captain took a cast of the lead while you were away in the boat, so he told me, and he got bottom at sixty-four fathoms."

"But even then," I muttered in a bewildered sort of way.

"It seems strange," he conceded, "but I'll explain it. When the brig was overwhelmed and the deck load was washed away, anchors, cables, and windlass all went with it. As is the fashion in those little vessels, the cables were stowed in troughs on the deck, but the ends were shackled to the keelson below, and they held. So there was the brig with both anchors hanging plumb down, and a hundred and twenty fathoms of cable out on each. The brig was then in very deep water, of course, and it was the weight of the anchors and cables that took her head down so low in the water ; also it was that that kept her head-on to wind and sea, otherwise what was left above the water would have fallen off into the trough and been swamped."

It took some little time for this information to soak in ; then I asked him how the accident had happened.

"I had overrun my little brig, I'll not deny it," he said. "I reckon that I know the Western Ocean as well as any one ; man and boy I've sailed it, winter and summer, for forty years. I've never been off it since I first went to sea, never served in a South Spainer, and never crossed the Line. Yet the Western Ocean plays curious pranks at times on those that know it best, and this was one of them. The brig was homeward-bound from Quebec to the Clyde with a full cargo of timber below and a heavy deck load besides. We had had fair sou'-westerly winds all the way and were making a good passage ; and although it was blowing half a gale at eight o'clock on that awful night, the glass was steady, and there was no sign of a change. At that time she was running along at about nine knots, with both fore and main upper and lower top-sails on her and a full foresail, and I thought that she would do nicely like that for the night. I was mistaken.

"By half-past eight the wind had freshened almost to a full gale, and the glass was dropping fast. I had to call all hands to get the canvas off her, and at midnight the wind was terrific and the seas were running like mountains. It was never properly dark that night. There was almost a full moon, although, of course, we never saw it, as it was obscured by clouds, but its light made the night seem more weird than ever. It helped the men with their work, but it also revealed to them the height of the tremendous waves and the inky-black scud racing at furious speed across the sky. By that time the brig had been shortened down, and was now under the main lower top-sail and a reefed foresail, and I also had the fore-topmast stay-sail set with the weather sheet well flat as well as the lee one, to pay her head off if she were caught by the lee, or commenced to broach-to. I still had all hands on deck, and as you may imagine they hadn't been idle, for sail after sail had been clewed up and furled since half-past eight, and the hands were pretty well played out. A gust of hurricane force exceeding anything that had preceded it showed me that I had run the brig too long, and that, if any of us were to see the dawn, she must at all costs be hove-to. The first job was to get the reefed foresail off her, and after a terrible struggle, during which I took the wheel myself and sent the helmsman to help the others, it was hauled up and furled. The brig was running with the wind on the starboard quarter, and I determined to try and heave her to on the starboard tack—which in any case was the right one—under a goose-winged main top-sail, for I did not believe that she would stand up to a full one.

" I was relieved from the wheel, and while the mate was hauling up the weather clew of the topsail preparatory to goose-winging it, I went below into the little cabin. There was a locker off it in which we kept new coils of rope for the running rigging, and I wanted to cut a good length of inch and half rope for a lashing for the top-sail. The first thing that I noticed in the rays of the lamp, which was swinging crazily, was that the cabin floor was littered with ship's biscuits. The man who was doing the combined job of cook and steward —he was now on deck in his oilskins toiling along-side of his shipmates—had opened a large tin that evening, and had carelessly left it on the table, from which it had rolled off. I remember feeling irritated about it—I never dreamt that his care-lessness would result in providing me with the necessary food to keep me alive. I had just cut off the length of rope which I required when I felt the shock of a tremendous wave striking the vessel, and heard a succession of crashes above the roar of the gale. At the same time the door of the companion-way was burst open, I became envel-oped in water, and the light went out.

"I managed to find my way to the foot of the companion-way, for there was a faint square of light showing in the inky darkness of the cabin, and fought my way up the stairs against the rush-ing water until I reached the deck. I looked for-ward. My God! Mr Norris, there was nothing to be seen but sea and sky; my brig seemed to have completely disappeared. Where the masts and yards and straining main top-sail and fore-topmast stay-sail had been, there was nothing but black flying clouds. I looked aft—there was noth-ing there but the deserted wheel, from which the man must have been washed away. I soon found out that not a thing remained above the water but about twenty feet of the after-deck, and that my men had all gone. I staggered to the wheel, not that I thought of steering, but I could see nothing else to hang on to, then something brushed against my legs; it was the dog. He must have been washed out of his kennel forward, and had probably been overboard too, but he is a powerful swimmer. All night I hung on to that wheel, which was jolting so much, in spite of the relieving tackles, that it nearly tore the arms out of me. I never, of course, expected to see daylight, but thought every moment that the brig would founder under my feet.

"The dawn took a long, long time to break, but at last daylight came, and I saw the brig just as she was when you saw her. During part of the night masts and spars still secured to her by the rigging had been hanging alongside and bumping into her, but by this time they had all been swept away. I collected my thoughts and tried to puzzle out how the thing had happened. The fore-top-mast stay-sail must have carried away, and the brig had broached-to with a terrific swerve; the deck load had gone overboard, carrying the lower masts and rigging with it. I couldn't understand at first why she was keeping head to wind and float-ing so deep forward until I thought of the anchors and chains. Of course, with any other cargo but timber she would have sunk like a stone, but she had just sufficient reserve buoyancy left to keep the after part of her floating above the waves. I felt that I could hang on to the wheel no longer, and

I

although I considered that my case was hopeless, I lashed myself to a ring-bolt in the covering board alongside the port bulwark with the length of rope which I had cut. The dog took up his position abaft the cabin skylight, the after end of which was standing above the water.

"I began to feel hungry, and presently noticed a couple of biscuits floating up from the direction of the companion-way. One floated close to me, and I grabbed it; the dog got the other. A few more floated up, which the dog at my bidding retrieved and brought to me. How many days I lived like that I cannot at present tell. When I feel stronger I'll reckon them up, but we must have drifted to the eastward a long way, and it was only the evening before you took me off the brig that I felt that the anchors had brought her up somewhere. They dragged for some considerable time before they held, and I had, of course, no idea where we were. I hardly ever felt thirsty, for I was wet through the whole time, but when I did I soaked my handkerchief when it rained and sucked it. I suffered a lot from cramp, but, strangely enough, I slept a good deal; in fact, I was asleep when your steamer was passing, until the dog woke me up with its barking. It wasn't until your boat was alongside that I found that—for the time being—I had lost my power of speech."

Completely fascinated I had listened to the old chap's tale, and I marvelled how he had lived and preserved his reason through all his hardships. He did not look at all robust, even allowing for the fact that he had not yet recovered from his partial

fasting and exhaustion, but he must have had the
heart of a lion. I hardly knew what to say to him,
but fell back on a question which between seamen
is quite a common one, but which might have been
considered impertinent as between landsmen.

" What will you do now ? " I asked. " Get
another ship ? "

" God knows, Mr Norris," he replied quietly. " I
fully expect that my owners will offer me one, but
after twenty years in command of the *Marion* . . .
She was a fine vessel, Mr Norris. You didn't see
her quite at her best."

A faint smile flitted across the old chap's face.
I believe that under different circumstances I would
have found that he possessed a keen sense of
humour.

" But," he continued, " you ought to have seen
her with every stitch of canvas on her, belting
through the Gut of Canso, outward-bound for
Miramichi. A lovely ship, Mr Norris. She would
go to windward like a yacht, and she was as strongly
built as a whaler."

I probably *had* seen her. If not, I had seen
dozens of her sisters of all sizes, beating up the Gulf
of St Lawrence in ballast or rolling home across
the Western Ocean with deck loads half-way up
to their lower yards ; and to be perfectly candid
there wasn't a fine ship amongst them. Most of
them leaked like sieves, so that they wouldn't have
been trusted with any other cargo but timber, and
all of them had their bows disfigured by having
square ports cut in them for the loading and discharging of logs. And yet . . .

TALES OF A PILOT SERVICE.

I. AT THE MOUTH OF THE RIVER.

THE river which is the scene of these tales is one of the most dangerous in all Asia.   Seen at high water, it is a noble-looking river, a mile and a half wide at its mouth, flowing in a stream which is unbroken from bank to bank.   At low water, however, it presents a different aspect—the hidden dangers, which high tide had treacherously concealed, become visible.   Mud-banks stand ten to twelve feet out of the water, and the navigable channels have contracted to, in some cases, less than a quarter of a mile.   Through these channels the brown muddy current sweeps at a force which reaches eight knots an hour, while swirling eddies will sometimes throw a large vessel athwart the river even against the pressure of her rudder. During spring tides the water will rise and fall as much as twenty-one feet, and a vessel which goes ashore at the top of high water, unless she can be promptly got off, has little chance of surviving through the hours of the following ebb tide.   With one part of her suspended on a mud-bank and the water rapidly receding and scouring the mud from under the other part, it is almost a certainty that she will break her back and become a total wreck.

To add to the natural dangers, during the south-west monsoon blinding rain squalls will suddenly blot out the banks of the river, concealing leading marks, beacons, buoys, and lights ; while during the early months of spring dense fogs often prevail in the mornings. To cope with all these dangers a highly-trained and efficient pilot service is maintained.

The pilotage extends over a distance of forty miles, and may roughly be divided into two sections —the river itself, and the estuary, which includes the outer bar. From the port, which is twenty-two miles up the river, and which has a bar immediately below it which deeply loaded vessels can cross only at high water, the river winds through a series of narrow channels, with here and there a broad reach. The channel just inside the mouth is the narrowest of all ; it runs between the right bank, which there is steep-to, and a vast shoal which lies off it. Below the point at the mouth of the river, on which there is a signal station, a spit extends for about three miles, and parallel to this spit there is a deep broad reach called the Spit channel, which, however, has a nasty cross-current. The outer end of this is marked by a light-vessel, and there a right-angled turn leads down to the outer bar, whose depths are constantly varying, as the silt from the river is either deposited or scoured away by the strong tides. The Spit channel affords a welcome anchorage when such is necessary, shallow water on the bar, and narrow channels in the river, making it difficult to anchor elsewhere. The pilot vessel usually lies at anchor six miles off the low palm-fringed coast, and about eighteen miles from the mouth of the river.

To the pilot vessel there came at four o'clock one morning in early March the mail steamer from another important port on the coast. She was well loaded with a valuable cargo, and had about a thousand native deck passengers on board. It was getting on for high water, the flood tide was almost finished, and it was still dark. As she slowed down a boat from the pilot vessel pushed off to her, one of the pilots was soon on board, and the steamer was then headed full speed on her course.

" You are rather late," said the pilot to her commander after he had reached the bridge and the usual greetings had been exchanged. " Better tell the engineer to give her all he can, or we may miss the tide."

" I was afraid of that," the captain agreed. " I sent down orders to let her go all out as soon as you got on board."

The captain of the mail steamer was a frequent trader to the port, and was well known to the pilot. He was deeply religious, and with rare moral courage carried his religion into the daily life of the vessels he commanded. Sailors are very apt to seize on any outstanding characteristic in order to find a nickname, and while respected all over the coast, he was universally known as Holy Joe. His religion has nothing to do with this incident, except that, in the opinion of those who knew him best, it inspired him with courage of a different nature, for he was a daring seaman, his daring amounting almost to audacity at times, and he would take risks that others, who had not his moral equipment, would shun. The pilot, for another reason, was rather inclined to be reckless, a very bad fault in a pilot, and one that few of them possess. Their whole training and responsibilities tend to eliminate this trait, and rather are they wont to inspire confidence by their careful trustworthiness. Recklessness, where found, is, as in this case, usually due to one cause—youth, and this cause is, especially in the East, soon removed. Enough has been told of the characters of both the captain and the pilot to show that, competent officers although both of them were, they were hardly an ideal combination to be rushing full speed in a high-powered steamer toward the mouth of a dangerous river on a morning that was already inclined to be hazy.

"Do you think we will manage to catch the tide, pilot?" inquired the captain.

"Yes, bar fog," was the reply.

"Fog! I don't see any sign of fog. It seems as clear as a bell; look at the stars overhead."

Resisting the temptation to repeat the time-honoured joke, and realising that humour under the circumstances would be misplaced, the pilot thoughtfully rubbed his hand along the iron rail which ran round the bridge. It was already moist, as if with sweat, a fairly sure indication of coming mist. By this time they had picked up, and were steering for, the light-vessel which marks the entrance to the Spit channel. Four steamers had gone in earlier on the tide, the last one only half an hour before, but there was no sign of any of their lights now. As they approached the light-vessel, the pilot looked in vain for the next set of leading lights. These, when in line, led through the narrow channel on the right bank, just inside the entrance. It was evident that a bank of fog was lying right across the mouth of the river. Shortly afterwards he heard a bell being rung violently, followed by two or three others. At least some of the vessels which had preceded them were at anchor in the Spit channel.

That was the time when the pilot should have come to a definite decision and anchored also. The pilots of those other vessels were more experienced than he, and they certainly would not have anchored there if they could have got in ; they had adopted the prudent course in an approach that was full of dangerous cross-currents. Still the pilot was loth to miss the tide, and perhaps a bit too sure of himself. He did take the precaution of ordering the engines to slow, but thought that he would stand in just a little farther and try to pick up the lights. The voice of the tempter at his elbow strengthened him in this idea.

" It will be breaking day in a few minutes, and we may manage to pick up something," suggested the captain, always eager to get on.

They had slowly passed three vessels at anchor, locating them only by the sound of their bells, and the pilot had just made up his mind that it wasn't good enough, and was about to give orders to anchor also, when there was a sudden exclamation from the captain—

I 2

" There are the lights, pilot, five on the port bow."

" Good," said the pilot, with a brief glance at the lights. " Full speed ahead."

As he gave the order he also told the man at the wheel to starboard the helm, so as to bring the lights on the other bow, for they had seemed to him somewhat open, and he wanted to run them into line so that they would lead him fairly up the channel. He and the captain then moved over to the port side of the bridge, and were peering through the mist in the half light to try and pick up the palm-trees on the bank at the mouth of the river, when a startled shout from the chief officer drew their attention to the other side.

" These are not the leading lights, pilot; they are fishing boats; we are nearly on top of them."

" Stop the engines, stand by the anchor," said the pilot, and then gave a gasp of dismay, for, as he watched the fishing boats surging past, he saw, not on the port side at all but broad on the starboard bow, the palm-trees looming through the fog and quite close. Instead of entering the river they were heading straight across the mouth of it for the spit outside. There was only one thing to do, go full speed astern, and the pilot gave the order for it. He almost immediately followed it with another. " Ring her up."

This last order may require a little explanation. The engineer officer in charge of the engine-room usually keeps a little reserve power in hand, and the double ring on the telegraph from the bridge to the engine-room signifies an emergency when every ounce of power is required.

The moments that followed were bitter ones for the pilot. From the way that the nearer objects on the beach appeared to be slipping aft past the farther ones, much as they seem to do when one is in a railway train, he could see that, although the engines were going stern, the vessel had still a lot of headway due to his mad rush full speed ahead when he thought he had seen the leading lights. He doubted if she could be brought up in time, and he knew that if she took the mud there, nothing could save her, for it was now after high water, and in a short time the ebb tide would be coming down like a sluice. In imagination he could already see the decks buckling under them, the terrified stampede of the deck passengers, the difficulty of rescue ; for even if the vessels at anchor near them tried to send their boats, these could do almost nothing in the scour of the strong current, and the same thing applied to the vessel's own boats. The fore-deck just immediately below him was packed with coolies, their families, baggage, and cooking pots. Many of the coolies were already awake, and, with their heads muffled up to keep out the chill morning air, were pointing excitedly at the shore. They were totally unaware of their danger : they were merely stirred by the first glimpse of the country of their adoption.

Inwardly he cursed himself for his folly in standing on so far, and to add to his bitterness of mind a loud peal on the bell of the nearest, though invisible, vessel at anchor came across to him through the fog. He envied the pilot of her, *he* had no greater responsibility at the time than to see that the bell was kept ringing ; in fact, he was probably sitting comfortably in the captain's cabin.

During the time, a matter of not many seconds, that these thoughts were chasing each other through his mind, he was keenly watching the beach, which gave the best indication of what the vessel was doing. They were so close that he could almost look down on it. In the foreground the muddy water was lapping against the bank, which was covered with rank grass, with here and there a few stunted bushes ; beyond was the signal station, with its tall mast, fringed by a belt of palm-trees, the nearer palms showing quite distinctly, the farther ones melting into the white fog, which lay in a dense mass over the land and all around them. Apparently calm, the only signs of strain about him were where his knuckles were showing white as his hands gripped the iron rail of the bridge like a vice ; at the same time he was leaning backward as if with his own strength he was trying to keep the vessel from striking the mud. The calm voice of Holy Joe fell like a sedative on his jangled nerves—

" She will bring up in time, pilot. Providence is on our side."

As he uttered the words, however, the pilot noticed that he gave the telegraph handle still another ring in case the engineer might have yet a little more power up his sleeve. By now, however, the engines were all out ; the funnels, bridge rails, and ventilators were shaking and rattling with the powerful vibration of them. The pilot could now see that the vessel had almost lost her headway, but could not tell, for the moment, whether she had brought up on the spit or not, for, although the man at the lead immediately below the bridge was giving a depth of six fathoms, or thirty-six feet, it was a steep shelving bank, and she might easily be aground forward. Suddenly his heart seemed to leap; surely the motion of the objects on the bank was reversed, the nearer objects, the stunted bushes, were drawing forward past the palm-trees; slowly, just perceptibly at first, then more rapidly. The movement was soon confirmed by an exultant yell from the man at the lead, " Going astern, sir."

Inwardly hoping that no other reckless fool like himself, into whom he could barge stern first, was nosing his way up the channel, the pilot quietly and carefully backed out into deep water, then, locating the position of one of the other vessels at anchor by the sound of her bell, he thankfully anchored just astern of her.

" I suppose we can do nothing now," said the captain.

" Only keep the bell ringing forward," replied the pilot. " What about a spot of coffee ? " As he spoke he wiped his brow with a handkerchief held in a hand that now decidedly trembled.

" Well, we have lost the tide after all," remarked the captain dolefully.

" It's a damned long way—I beg your pardon," said the pilot, remembering the character of his companion. " It's a long way better to lose the tide than lose the ship."

II. THE PRIZE SHIP.

During the second week of July 1914 the large cargo steamer *Alesia* of the Hamburg-America Line left Germany for the port referred to in these tales. She passed through the Suez Canal on the 26th July, and signalled off Perim on the 30th. At the outbreak of war there was no naval vessel at the port, but the marine and military authorities looked up the *Alesia* in Lloyd's Register, and discovered that she was fitted with wireless. This was confirmed by those in the port, who were in a position to know, for she had been there before. The authorities then very naturally decided that she would make for a neutral port, probably in the Dutch East Indies, and if she managed to elude our own and the Japanese cruisers, would there intern herself.

The day after war was declared the sailing pilot vessel was withdrawn and replaced by a small, fast, coasting steamer. This steamer could run into the river in the event of her sighting an enemy cruiser, which might attempt to hamper the trade of the port by capturing the pilots who would be on board. On the afternoon of the 12th August, just after a heavy rain squall which had blotted everything out for about an hour had passed over, to the amazement of every one on board, the *Alesia* was sighted close to, standing toward the pilot vessel, and flying the German pilot jack at the fore. The anchor on the pilot vessel was hove up, and she prepared to make a run for it in case the stranger should be armed. She appeared, however, to be quite peaceful, and the first thing that the pilots noticed was that she had no wireless apparatus aloft. She stopped under the pilot vessel's stern in the ordinary way, and a pilot was sent off to her.

Fortunately, the pilot who was on turn for duty, although quite junior, was a man of cool resource, and, moreover, he had a face which had the faculty of concealing all emotion. As he was being pulled across in the boat from the pilot vessel to the steamer, he realised, however, that he would need all his wits about him if he were to carry the job to a successful conclusion. There were two problems to be faced. The first was that the stranger might, after all, be armed with well-concealed guns, that he might intend to try and get up the river to a position from which he could bombard the large oil installation, and thus do tremendous damage before he would be inevitably sunk by the guns from the forts. The pilot decided that if there were any evidence of this he would run the vessel on to the most dangerous shoal he could find, and take the consequences. The second and more likely case was that the commander of the *Alesia* was not aware that war had broken out, and the pilot's duty would then be to conceal this information, take the vessel up the river, and anchor her under the guns of the nearest fort.

On reaching the bridge of the steamer he discovered that the captain and chief officer were the same as on a previous voyage when he had been the pilot, and the former, in the manner of men making port after a long voyage, was eager for news. The captain and all his officers spoke English, but with the strong American accent which they seem to acquire in Trans-Atlantic vessels.

" I see you have a new pilot boat. Where is the old sailing vessel ? " was the captain's first remark after the *Alesia* had been headed on her course.

" She was sunk in collision with a big tramp last week," replied the pilot.

" Well, that's too bad. Any one drowned ? "

The pilot nodded his head sadly. " Four pilots and half the crew," he said, following up his remark by a vivid description of the mythical disaster and a scathing criticism of the seamanship of the commander of the tramp steamer.

The captain, after expressing his sympathy, asked for a newspaper, but for obvious reasons the pilot hadn't got one. He, however, invented a typhoon which had wiped out the half of Hong-Kong and an equally disastrous earthquake in South America. He also elicited the information that the *Alesia's* wireless had been dismantled for repairs in Hamburg, and had not been ready when they left—a great inconvenience to them.

" By the way," said the captain, " is there any war in Europe ? "

" Never heard of one," said the pilot. " Why ? "

" When I left Suez, Austria had sent an ultimatum to Servia over the murder of that Archduke, and Russia was looking real nasty."

" Oh, that fizzled out," said the pilot.

" Well, I guess I'll go below and have a little nap. I haven't had much sleep for the last two days with this darned old monsoon of yours."

Left to himself, the pilot gazed around. He had often been on board of German ships before, but now he noticed things with a new interest. He saw signs of efficiency everywhere : the vessel was well painted, and all her gear was in good condition. The sailors, who were doing odd jobs about the decks, seemed to be a docile, willing lot. They were men of good physique, clean and tidy. All wore the typical small white cap. The strict discipline of the pre-war German mercantile marine was in evidence. Soon afterwards the chief officer came up on the bridge and entered into conversation with him.

" Was the old man talking to you about war ? " he asked.

" He did mention it," the pilot admitted.

" He makes me ill at times. Why, all this about war between England and Germany is newspaper talk, pilot. For one thing, our Socialists wouldn't allow a war, and quite right too. They wouldn't get me to fight for a lot of capitalists."

The pilot readily agreed, although at the moment that the chief officer had interrupted his thoughts, he had been considering ways and means of getting to England to join the New Army, for he had been a keen officer in the local volunteer battalion for years. Could the chief officer have looked into his bag he would have seen, at the bottom of it, well-thumbed copies of ' Field Service Regulations ' and ' Infantry Training—1914.'

By this time they were approaching the light-vessel at the entrance to the Spit channel, so the pilot gave instructions to hoist the ship's number and the ensign. After a slight delay this was acknowledged by the answering pennant on the flag-staff of the signal station, and he knew that the fact that the *Alesia* was in the river would be promptly telegraphed up to the port. There was something else, however, to cause him anxiety, and that was the scene on the bank at the entrance to the river. Usually deserted except for the signal station and a few water buffaloes, it had been since the 4th of August, when it was occupied by a double company of Indian infantry, a regular hive of industry. The signal station itself was heavily sand-bagged, and trenches had been dug above high-water mark, which would be certain to be manned as they passed. A cluster of white tents stood out in sharp contrast to the dark green of the palms, and, to make matters worse, the clear notes of a bugle came across the water just as they were approaching the point. The pilot did not wait for inquiries ; he decided to take the initiative.

" The annual military manœuvres are on," he told the chief officer. " Those fellows like to play at being real soldiers at times."

Beyond passing a remark about the dreariness of the spot and the probable dampness of the trenches, the chief officer, to the pilot's relief, did not appear to be interested. To give point to his words a black squall, a moving mass of wind and rain, came howling up from the sea. It quickly passed over the little camp, completely hiding it from view, and sweeping up the river, shut out everything outside a radius of a hundred yards. The engines were ordered to slow, the hand lead kept going, and they cautiously felt their way up the river until the squall passed as quickly as it had arrived. When the weather had cleared, the chief officer seemed to have forgotten all about the camp, for he started to yarn about his domestic affairs : he was going to be married at the end of this voyage, also he was to get his first command. Life looked very rosy to him.

A little farther up the river was the examination vessel, a large launch from which representatives of the marine and military authorities examined neutral vessels, and also gave daily a combination of flags to all ships to hoist to enable them to pass the forts. As this vessel had no guns, the pilot was not surprised when she modestly withdrew higher up the river on their approach. Vessels, even in peace time, were not allowed to cross the bar just below the port after dark, and this furnished him with a good excuse for anchoring in the river ; so, just as the sun was setting, he brought the *Alesia* up just off the lower fort, and about seven miles below the city.

Soon after they anchored he went into the saloon to dinner, and there met the other officers. With the exception of the chief engineer they were quite an agreeable lot, and all, save that individual, politely carried on the conversation in English. He, however, contributed a number of surly remarks in German, the only occasion on which he spoke English being when the pilot, in explanation of the fact that the searchlight from the fort was playing on them continuously, while higher up the river the ray from another one swept at intervals across the sky, again mentioned the military manœuvres. He then with a sneer suggested that if the British army officials had any sense they would not hold their manœuvres in the rainy season, a remark which contained so much truth in it that the pilot did not try to answer it.

" Our chief engineer has been' in the German army," said the captain, but whether he meant the remark as an excuse for that officer's rudeness, or to show that he spoke with authority, the pilot could not guess.

On the plea that it was a warm night, and that in any case he wished to be handy should the vessel sheer heavily at anchor, the pilot declined a stateroom, but had a camp-bed laid out for him on the lower bridge just outside the captain's cabin. About ten o'clock he lay down, having previously warned the chief officer that, owing to the quarantine regulations, he must not lower the gangway ladder, or allow any one on board without permission. All the Germans in the vicinity had been collected and interned during the first two or three days of the war, but there was just a chance that some native in their employ might get to know of the vessel being in the river, and contrive to give a warning. For some time after he had lain down he could hear scraps of a conversation being carried on upon the bridge above him between the chief engineer and the captain. The former was apparently vehemently trying to drive some argument home, while the captain was placidly endeavouring to refute it.

The pilot had little sleep that night. Every sound in the engine-room caused him to start nervously with the idea that they were opening the sea-cocks. Once or twice when he got up and looked over the side he even imagined that the vessel was deeper in the water ; if she were sunk there it would be rather disastrous, as she would partially block the channel. The searchlight from the fort flashed on them incessantly. In the early hours of the morning, however, he dropped off into a troubled sleep, but was wakened at the first streak of dawn by the chief officer.

" There is some one in a large launch alongside, pilot. He wants the gangway lowered."

" That will be the port health officer," said the pilot. " Lower away and let him on board."

He lay on the camp-bed and listened ; in the still morning air he could hear the ropes of the gangway ladder tackle running through the blocks, and the ladder itself bumping down the vessel's side, and shortly afterwards the tramp of ammunition boots on the ladder and on the deck. There was a great shuffling of feet, and then—

" Stand at—ease. Stand—easy."

He got up and looked down on the fore-deck. Drawn up in two long lines, one on each side, were two platoons of British infantry. As he stood there the captain came out of his cabin; at last there was a note of alarm in his voice.

" What is the meaning of this, pilot ? " he asked.

" I regret to say, captain, it means that your country is at war with mine, and that your ship has been captured."

As he spoke a figure dashed past him; it was the chief engineer making for the engine-room, presumably intent on doing whatever damage he could while he still had a chance. With a quick shout to the military officers who were coming up the iron ladder from the fore-deck to the lower bridge, the pilot rushed along the deck, and, collaring the engineer low, brought him down with a thud just as he was about to enter the engine-room door.

About an hour afterwards a crew drawn from the ships in the harbour came on board, and the vessel was moved up to a permanent berth. Before leaving her the pilot went along to the saloon to bid good-bye to the captain, and on his way he had to pass the chief engineer's cabin. Through the open door, which was guarded by two soldiers, he could see the chief engineer, and stopped for a moment to sympathise with him. The engineer was not apparently in a conversational mood, for his reply was brief and to the point.

" *Schweinhund*," he said.

The captain was very much depressed at the loss of his ship, and at the prospect of having to spend some considerable time in an internment camp, but he roused himself as the pilot entered the saloon.

" Have you ever played poker, pilot ? " he asked.

" Yes, occasionally. Why ? "

" Because with that face of yours all you have to do is go across to the States, start right in, and make a fortune. The pilot vessel sunk last week and four pilots drowned—poor fellows ; never heard of a war in Europe ; military manœuvres—*Gott in Himmel.*"

That was the pilot's first encounter with Germans during the war, but he was destined to have many more. Shortly after this incident he went to England, and before very long he was in France. After being twice wounded he again went into the line, and finally fell riddled by machine-gun bullets while leading a platoon of a famous Highland regiment on the Somme. There he lies in a soldier's grave, while on the mainmast of the old sailing pilot vessel, which has since been replaced by an up-to-date steamer, can be seen a brass plate to his memory.

III. THE PARIAH BRIG.

Many years ago there were two distinct types of sailing vessels trading round the Indian coast. These were known to seafarers as the " country ships," which, although mostly owned by Indians, were officered by Europeans, and had large well-trained Lascar crews, and the " pariahs," which were owned, officered, and manned entirely by natives. Many of the former strove, not without success, to emulate in style, splendour, and discipline, the old East Indiamen, but they have long since disappeared from the face of the waters. The " pariahs " were never so ambitious, but there were many smart little vessels amongst them, and their native crews were generally composed of good seamen. A number of them still survive, but they have deteriorated ; year by year they become more shabby and dilapidated ; more long splices are seen in their coir running gear, less paint on their sun-dried wooden hulls, and more jagged tears in their copper. In certain trades, which it would hardly pay the steamers to enter, they still seem to pick up a precarious living.

One of those trades is that between the Nicobar Islands—where they load green cocoanuts, using

their own boats as lighters—and various ports in
India, and up till the time of the war it was a common thing for three or four of them to turn up at
the pilot station on one day, usually at the end of
the south-west monsoon. They were mostly
barques and brigs, and their advent was never
very popular, for, apart from the uncertainty as to
how long they would take to get up the river, they
were generally rather dirty, and the pilot had to
take his own food, and even water, on board. Prior
to the war, however, all the pilots had received
their earlier training in sailing ships, and took a
pride in their ability to handle them. When a
number of " pariahs " arrived on the station together they would almost invariably be sailed all
the way up the river. Many exciting races took
place, and the almost forgotten art of backing and
filling a vessel through a narrow channel with the
tide, but against a head wind, would often be
revived. Most of the younger generation of pilots
received their early training in steamers ; they
know practically nothing about handling vessels
under sail, and even if they did, the gear of the
" pariahs " and their crews are no longer reliable.
Moreover, time is more important nowadays, so
now, when a sailing vessel comes to the station, the
pilot usually exercises the prerogative given him
by the rules of the port, and orders it to anchor
until a steam tug can be obtained.

One day in October a tall pile of canvas coming
in before the sea breeze was observed from the
pilot vessel, and in the afternoon the native brig
Karnul backed her main yard, and hove-to along-

side, awaiting a pilot. The pilot who was on turn, although one of the younger men, knew how to handle a sailing vessel, but still had no desire to spend longer than necessary on board a " pariah." Before going off to her he decided that, as there was a fair wind blowing, and it was flood tide, he would sail her up into the river, but he requested the next pilot who was on turn, and who was making ready to board an incoming steamer, to wireless a message up to town to send a steam tug down to meet him. When going off in the boat he noticed that she was cleaner and smarter-looking than most vessels of her class, but he could not remember having seen her before. Climbing up the short rope ladder he got on board, and was greeted by the master, a tall powerfully-built native, who seemed unable to understand any language which the pilot could speak. He had with him, however, a native of about thirty, who spoke good English, as an interpreter, although he also seemed to carry out the duties of cabin boy. The master received with delight the pilot's decision to sail up into the river, the yards were squared, and a course set up the channel.

The pilot requested that a small awning be spread to keep the sun off him, and this was done. He was also given a chair, and, taking a magazine out of his bag, he settled down to read, glancing up occasionally to see that the brig was kept on her course. About four o'clock he was interrupted by the interpreter, who said—

" Master like a cup of tea, sir."

Rather surprised, for this was unusual on board

a " pariah," the pilot said that " master " would, and soon afterwards the interpreter brought a tray with tea, sugar, tinned milk, and biscuits. This was the first time that he noticed that there was something vaguely familiar both about the face of the interpreter and about his speech.

The wind holding favourable, they made good progress, passed the light-vessel, and entered the Spit channel. Here the pilot had his hands full, for there was a strong current setting across it on to a shoal, but, by skilful handling, he managed to weather the point on which stood the signal station, and then stood on up the river. The wind soon afterwards fell away a little, but there was still enough to keep the sails full. The *Karnul* was quite a fast little vessel, with good lines and a large spread of canvas, and with the last drain of the flood tide under her, was gliding along at a good pace. The pilot sat in his chair contentedly smoking and watching the bank slipping past. Occasionally he would glance aloft to see that all the yards were properly trimmed and the sails drawing. On the port hand the rice-fields extended away to the misty horizon, broken here and there by belts of jungle on the banks of the intersecting creeks. The sun was fast dropping, and deepening the yellow of the ripening paddy, and finally sunk, a ball of fire, its last rays flashing on the gilded cones of the small pagodas which were dotted here and there about the fields. In the twilight the sails changed in tint from white to dark grey, but it was short, and soon they were showing black against the glittering stars.

About an hour afterwards the ebb tide came down so strongly that the brig could no longer make headway, so, being then in a broad reach, the pilot sheered her in toward the shore out of the track of shipping, and ordered the anchor to be let go and the sails clewed up and furled. The interpreter took some of the food which the pilot had brought on board to the galley to be cooked, and it was while the latter was eating this meal that he suddenly remembered where he had met the native before. During the war he had been a pilot of a different kind, for he had gone to England and joined what was then the Royal Flying Corps. Quickly getting his wings, he went to France, and after a brief but exciting career, he was brought down behind the German lines, and was for two years a prisoner of war in various prison camps. It was in the last of these that he had met the interpreter, and that individual had always been a mystery to him. Obviously he did not belong to any of the fighting races of India, and was not a prisoner of war, but seemed to hang about the camp and do odd jobs. On several occasions the pilot had heard him talk German, and believed that he was there to spy upon the British officers. Certainly he got several of them, who became familiar with him, into trouble, but the pilot, having lived in the East, did not make that mistake. Just before the Armistice, Putriah, for that was the name he went under, disappeared. When in Germany he had been dressed in a nondescript khaki uniform, and as he was now in native dress it is little wonder that the pilot had not at first recognised him. He had little fear that Putriah would know him. In those days he wore a moustache, now he was clean shaven again, and besides, he was much stouter.

Although the brig was fairly clean, the pilot did not fancy sleeping in the saloon, so ordered a sail to be laid out on deck, and this made a comfortable bed. It was a glorious night, with a light warm breeze, and after lying for some time listening to the wavelets lapping against the side of the brig, he fell asleep.

About four o'clock in the morning he woke up, and glancing forward, noticed that some one was waving a lantern slowly over the side. Soon afterwards he heard voices, and the sound of two boats being rowed toward the brig. He got up, strolled along the deck, and met Putriah.

" What do these boats want ? " he asked.

" The poor fellows would like some green cocoa-nuts, master," was the reply. " They say that they are very dear in the bazaar."

In addition to their other duties, the pilots are *ex officio* customs officers, and while their responsibilities in this respect are mainly nominal, they are supposed to see that no cargo is discharged in the river outside the recognised discharging places. The pilot was wondering whether he should interfere, or merely close his eyes to such an apparently harmless proceeding, when his cogitations were interrupted by a stentorian hail from the other side of—

" Brig ahoy ! " It was the steam tug which he had ordered.

" Hullo ! " he shouted.

" When do you want to start in ? "

" We can start right away," said the pilot. " The flood will have made before we get the anchor up."

Turning to Putriah, who by this time had been joined by the master and several of the crew, he told him to heave the anchor up and take the tug's hawser. This order was received by the master with what appeared to be a vehement protest.

" What does he say ? " asked the pilot.

" He says, master, that he does not want a tug. He wants to stay here until daylight and sail up the river."

" Tell him that it doesn't matter much what he wants," said the pilot pleasantly. " We will get under weigh and tow up at once."

On being told this the master flew into a violent temper, and waving his arms about, was evidently protesting vigorously when the pilot cut him short, and said curtly—

" Look here, I have had quite enough of this ; tell him that I will give him five minutes to start heaving aweigh. If he doesn't start by then, I will lash the tug-boat alongside, slip your cable, leave your anchor on the bottom of the river, and tow you up to town."

Putriah himself issued the orders, and led the indignant master into the saloon. As soon as they got under weigh the pilot went aft, told the man at the wheel to steer after the tug, and leant against the taffrail smoking a cigarette. In the saloon below he could hear Putriah and the master, but their positions seemed to be reversed, for it was the former who was speaking sternly, and the master was much more subdued. The pilot was rather mystified ; he wondered if this could possibly be the Putriah of the prison camp, and then he remembered a strange hobby which he had taken up as a prisoner of war—the collecting of finger-prints. He had dozens of them which he had obtained from fellow-prisoners, all certified, neatly pasted into a book, and labelled. Amongst them were those of Putriah, which he had obtained by a subterfuge, and he wondered if he could obtain another. Just then Putriah approached him full of conciliation, and asked, very politely, if he would like a cup of tea.

" Yes, please," said the pilot. " And if you will get me a bucket of water I will have a wash. You might take my bag down to the saloon, and I will wash there."

It was now daylight, and all the man at the wheel had to do was follow the tug. The pilot went below, and after having a wash, he asked Putriah if he had any boot blacking, as he had got his boots wet coming off in the boat. Putriah, apparently ready to do anything to please, went off for the blacking, and when he had gone, the pilot took the magazine from his bag, opened it in the middle, and folding it back, placed it on the deck some distance from the bag. He put his feet one after another on a bench, and when Putriah had finished the boots, the pilot asked him to rub the leather above one of his big toes, and try to soften it, as he had a painful corn. He then proceeded to pack his bag, and as he did so he said—

"Chuck me that magazine over, but don't lose the place."

To do this Putriah had to press the edges, and as he handed the magazine to the pilot, the latter was pleased to see some finger-prints, and more especially that of the thumb, on the margin.

They arrived in the harbour, and after handing the brig over to the berthing officials, the pilot went on shore. On arriving at his bungalow he found his book of finger-prints, took out the page with those of Putriah, and after a bath and breakfast, he got out his car and ran down to the office of his friend, the commissioner of police.

"The first thing to do obviously is to compare the prints," said that official. "We will send them down to the finger-print expert."

Calling a peon, he wrote a note and despatched it with the prints. The pilot then told him about the boats coming alongside in the river, and also about the scene made by the master when he had given orders to weigh the anchor.

"That looks as if your friend Putriah had turned to smuggling," said the commissioner. "It might be opium or cocaine, or both, although I cannot remember any of the native vessels being caught at it. However, that is a job for our friends, the Customs, and I shall warn them."

Just then the peon returned with a note—undoubtedly the finger-prints were identical.

"I will have friend Putriah carefully watched,"

said the commissioner. "If anything of interest happens I will let you know. Good-morning. Many thanks."

One evening two or three days later the pilot strolled into the club and saw, standing at the bar, the commissioner and two other men. On seeing the pilot he motioned him to an empty table, and soon joined him. After ordering drinks he said—

"Well, we safely jugged your friend Putriah and the master to-day—two of the most dangerous anarchists in India."

He went on further to relate that, warned by him, the Customs officers had thoroughly searched the brig. They had found no opium or cocaine, and were about to give up the search when one of them happened to ask about some green cocoa-nuts which were stowed apart from the cargo in a small hatch below the saloon. The ever-ready Putriah explained that they were special ones, which were to be used for seed. One of the officers casually picked up a cocoa-nut and found it to be as heavy as lead. A police guard was put on board, and the cocoa-nut taken up to the arsenal, where it was found to contain a powerful bomb. The outer skin had been cut to allow the bomb to be inserted, and very cleverly closed again. There were about a hundred of these bombs on board.

At the subsequent trial, when the pilot went into the witness-box, Putriah was apparently unconcerned. He even contrived a little smile of welcome. The second question put by the prosecutor to the pilot was—

" You were in 1918 a prisoner of war at ——, a prison camp in Germany ? "

Putriah's unconcern vanished. He gazed keenly at the pilot, and a sickly expression came over his face. For the first time he recognised his real conqueror.

THE SALVING OF THE *CHANG CHU*.

I.

THERE was another reason besides the one of economy that induced me to take a passage from Hong Kong to Singapore on the steamer *Chang Chu*, which was Chinese owned but under the British flag. In the days of my youth, before I had taken to soldiering, I had been a sailor, had served an apprenticeship in a sailing vessel, and had been a certificated, though very junior, officer in the Merchant Service. Those youthful days, full of discomfort as they had been, were nevertheless good to look back to, and I had always found that the officers of tramps were more companionable and readier to yarn over old times than those of liners, who, after all, have so many different types of passengers to deal with that it is difficult to win even their short-lived friendship.

I boarded the *Chang Chu* from a sampan in Hong Kong harbour about an hour before she was ready to sail. I was going on three months' leave to India, and had with me my Pathan orderly, Yakoub Khan, Afridi. She was a vessel of about 4000 tons deadweight, and rather old. In a very short space of time we had settled down. Although outwardly the ship was dirty, for she was still loading cargo, I found that her saloon, which in the old-fashioned style was right aft, was clean and tidy. She had only a few cabins, for even in her palmy days she did not carry many passengers, and one of those, a two-berthed one, I had to myself. She had a long raised poop above the saloon, on which were a few inviting-looking deck-chairs, so, having a good stock of the latest novels to reach Hong Kong, I looked forward to a pleasant laze for the next six days.

In the short space of time before we sailed, such is the Freemasonry of the sea, I had become acquainted with the captain, an elderly man, and his two officers, had had tea with the former in his cabin below the bridge, and even been invited to go on that sacred edifice when we were moving out of the harbour.

" Now this is better than all your liners," I said to myself, as, having left my coat in my cabin and rolled up my shirt sleeves, for it was rather warm, I lit a pipe and loafed out of the saloon. In the companion-way, however, my pipe came out of my mouth with a jerk, for coming down the staircase was a lady, the last thing in the world that I had expected to see. She glanced at me and passed on down into the saloon, accompanied by the Chinese chief steward, while I, not feeling so comfortable now, moved toward the bridge. Just as I reached it the anchor was being hove up.

We were anchored fairly close to the city, and now all my attention was taken up by the manœuvring of the vessel. With infinite skill the old skipper, now shaving a sampan, again altering his course slightly to avoid a lumbering junk under sail, gradually worked his way toward the more open channel. We passed the incoming P. & O. mail steamer, a real aristocrat of the sea, with her black hull and funnels and stone-coloured boats, deck houses, and fittings. She was crowded with passengers in all their shore-going finery, but I did not envy one of them as I lounged against the bridge rail, smoking my pipe, and enjoying every minute. Gradually the vista of Hong Kong's crowded harbour, with its thousands of Chinese junks and sampans, its coasting steamers, tramps, and liners, began to fade from view; we were dipping into the swell of the open sea, and I suddenly remembered the lady.

"You have another passenger," I remarked to the skipper.

"Yes, worse luck," he replied. "I didn't want her, but the Chinese agent on shore insisted. Every little helps these days. Unfortunately all my old boys have gone; with the exception of the chief steward, they are an entirely new lot. I have told him off to look after the lady himself. By the way, if you see any slackness don't hesitate to let me know. Anyhow, the sun is just about gone, and the second officer can take her now for a bit. What about having one?"

We descended into his cabin, and over a whisky-and-soda he told me some more of his troubles. It appeared that only two days ago some mysterious Trades Union, a secret society, had called out the whole of his crew. Sailors, firemen, cooks, boys, all had gone ; only the British officers and Chinese chief steward remained. He was rather worried over the whole affair, but admitted that up till now neither the chief engineer nor himself had had any cause for complaint. The new crew had been obtained through some agency that was just about as mysterious as the one that had called out the old.

At dinner that evening I met my fellow passenger. We were alone, for the captain could not leave the bridge for long, and the other officers did not appear. As she entered the saloon I had time to notice that she was slim and straight, rather above middle height, and I should say athletic. Her face, although distinctly beautiful, impressed me more than anything else as being alert and intelligent. I thought her age would be about twenty-seven. She wore a semi-evening dress of black velvet, which, although I am no judge of these matters, appeared to be the work of a pretty capable dressmaker.

After a pause we introduced each other, there being no one else to do it. We had not finished the soup when I noticed that the hands of Miss Browne, for that was her name, were in a deplorable state. One could imagine that she had decarbonised the cylinders and greased the springs of at least three cars during the past few days. Indeed she rather puzzled me, for, apart from these evidences of manual labour, she discussed in a ready and charming manner various topics of the East and of home.

Despite the captain's forebodings, the meal was an excellent one and well served, while the servants were clean and attentive. After dinner I invited Miss Browne to have a cigarette on the poop, and we strolled up and down together under the awning. I was not, however, displeased when, under the plea that she had had a strenuous day, she decided to turn in early, for I also was feeling that way. I had been through the usual series of late nights that one has before going on leave, and wasn't sorry to seek my bunk.

I found Yakoub Khan, who in the meantime had, as I expected, made himself very much at home, laying out his roll of bedding on the floor outside my cabin. I suggested a more comfortable place, but he merely smiled. Before turning in, while rummaging for some article that I wanted, I found his rifle cunningly concealed amongst my baggage. This supplied the clue to his choice of a sleeping place : a Pathan and his rifle are usually close companions.

The four days that followed were very peaceful and pleasant. The weather was calm, while the slight swell troubled neither my companion nor myself. At six o'clock in the morning a boy would waken me with " choti hazri," composed of tea, toast, and fruit. Shortly afterwards I was on the poop, which had been newly washed down, sniffing the fresh, cool, morning air. The first morning, remembering the presence of a lady, I had rather hesitated about venturing on deck in my usual attire on those occasions, pyjamas and dressing-gown, but to my satisfaction she soon joined me clad in the same way. We would walk smartly up and down the deck until eight, when she would go below, and I would do some physical jerks prior to bath and breakfast.

The rest of the day we mostly spent in long deck-chairs, and I began to find Miss Browne a sensible and pleasant companion. She neither expected to be entertained nor did she chatter. A pleasant breeze made by the vessel's progress through the water blew under the awning. As we reclined in our respective chairs we would exchange an occasional remark, drawing attention at times to some passage in our books, at others to some passing vessel. At noon I would go to the captain's cabin, where, after he had finished working up the ship's position, he would dispense an excellent cocktail, the recipe for which he promised me. Alas! I never got it.

The other two officers we hardly saw: they were on watch and watch, and needed all the rest they could get; while the chief engineer, who hailed from the Clyde, had got three months' football papers from a friend in a sugar-mill in Hong Kong, and divided his time between those and a game of Patience, which he called " Cheating the Chinaman."

The new crew seemed to have settled down quietly, and were giving no trouble, but I could see that the captain, an old China coaster, was puzzled over them. He said they were a superior sort of crowd, in fact rather too superior for his liking. He instanced the boatswain, whom he pointed out from the bridge. Slim, neat, quiet, even one would say gentlemanly, he was the very opposite to one's usual impression of that petty officer. On the other hand, the supercargo, a tall powerfully built Chinaman, with a weather-beaten face and a villainous squint, didn't resemble the part either. In fact, they would have looked more characteristic had their positions been exchanged.

On two occasions the captain joined in at dinner, and an entertaining companion the dear old chap was. On the second evening out, after dinner, a four at bridge being apparently out of the question, I proposed piquet to Miss Browne, and found her a very capable performer. On the last occasion on which we played I noticed that her hands had become more like what I thought a lady's hands should be.

It was on that night, after she had retired, as I was having a last drink and a cigarette in the saloon, that a quick warning from Yakoub Khan brought me to my feet, and I realised that the saloon had quickly filled with Chinese. In front of me, with a long knife drawn back to strike, was one whom I recognised as one of the quarter-masters. With a half-arm jolt I got him under the jaw, but, as the knife dropped from his hand and he slowly collapsed on the floor, some one from behind struck me a terrific blow on the head ; it felt as if it had been administered with a maul.

I can just remember as I went off a series of loud reports that sounded uncommonly like " five rounds rapid," and the acrid smell of cordite ; then came oblivion.

II.

How many short spells of consciousness I had before I finally came round to find myself reclining on some bags in pitch darkness I cannot remember. Once or twice I had felt a cool hand on my throbbing brow, and another time, with the aid of an electric torch, I had been fed with condensed milk and brandy. Now, although still shaky, I felt that I had almost recovered. I could feel—it was too dark to see—Miss Browne by my side. In answer to my inquiries, she told me that we had been down this hatch, which lay immediately beneath the saloon and was really a large storeroom, two nights and a day. My orderly was responsible for us being here. He had first dropped me down and had then seized her, struggling at first, for she had not understood, and thrown her down beside me.

The vessel had been anchored three hours after I had been felled; to the best of her knowledge all the other Europeans and the Chinese chief steward were dead, and the pirates—for such the crew had turned out to be—had been discharging the cargo ever since into two large sailing junks which had come alongside when we arrived. She believed that they had just cast off.

A moan somewhere in the vicinity caused me to start nervously.

" What's that ? " I asked.

" That," said Miss Browne, " is the man you laid out. He is one of the quartermasters. Your orderly also collected him, apparently in the belief that he would come in useful."

" Where is Yakoub Khan ? " I asked.

" Up on deck," she replied. " He has been about quite a lot. At present he is making sure that they have really gone."

Shortly afterwards the hatch was removed, which let in some light, and Yakoub Khan announced that it was safe to come up. Painfully we struggled up an iron ladder and emerged into the saloon, a very much washed-out-looking pair. A stentorian yell, " Iderao, China soor ki jat," from my orderly brought the Chinaman up in a hurry. Yakoub Khan had evidently put the fear of death into him.

Miss Browne thought that some strong tea would do us all good, so, taking the thoroughly subdued quartermaster, whose name it appeared was Ah Wong, with her, she went off to the galley. Sitting back in a chair, I received from my orderly a further account of what had happened.

All that Miss Browne had told me was correct. The captain and other officers had been murdered just before I was attacked. Something had roused Yakoub Khan's suspicions, and he had slipped into my cabin, put a clip of cartridges into the magazine of his rifle, and returned to the saloon just in time. His five shots had all taken effect, and then, doubt-less remembering a little mix-up that he and some others of his regiment had with the Prussians at Festubert, he had gone in with the butt, quickly cleared the saloon, and, throwing the dead and wounded outside, had locked the doors.

For the next three hours he had remained on guard, his rifle now fully charged ; but the pirates had made no further attempt to molest us, doubtless biding their time. Just after the vessel was anchored the bodies of the other Europeans had been thrown overboard, with the usual result in these shark-infested waters. About one o'clock in the morning, as the junks were coming alongside and the pirates were busy removing the hatches, Yakoub Khan had managed to drag three heavy bags of rice right aft on the poop, and had dropped them, one after another, with loud splashes into the sea. Then, being like many Pathans a bit of a ventriloquist, he had emitted a series of piercing shrieks before returning to the saloon by the skylight, which he then purposely left open. He had the satisfaction of hearing a boat lowered with a rush, and pulled round the stern, its occupants, I fancy, being more anxious to make sure that we were really dead than to make any attempt to rescue us.

I now felt strong enough to go on deck, and saw that we were anchored in a small strait between two islands. One of these was very small, the other large enough to be the mainland somewhere. From an approximate idea that I had of the ship's position on the night of the tragedy, however, I knew this to be impossible. There was a fresh breeze blowing from the south, and the sails of two large Chinese junks were disappearing round a headland of the large island. That, at any rate, was something to be thankful for.

I was not, however, allowed to remain thankful for very long. Yakoub Khan pointed out that they had only been able to take about half the cargo in the junks ; and the fact that they had carefully replaced the hatches and covered them with tarpaulins showed that they meant to return or perhaps other junks might turn up at any moment. This also explained why they had not taken the vessel out into deep water, opened the sea cocks, and destroyed all the evidence of their crime.

Here was a pretty predicament. I looked around the ship. They had taken away every boat, and after the news about the sharks, I certainly didn't relish the idea of a raft, even if we could have got anywhere with it. Just then Miss Browne and Ah Wong came along with tea, which did us a lot of good, and I began to feel more like myself. The others shortly afterwards disappeared, and I walked up and down the poop racking my still slightly fuddled brain, and also thinking of the dear old skipper and the others who had met their doom so swiftly and silently.

After half an hour of it I was still as far from any idea of how to escape as ever, when, from the front of the poop, I observed Miss Browne, clad in what appeared to be a dungaree boiler suit, and Yakoub Khan emerge from the engine-room. They came straight up to me.

" I think we will be able to move the old ship out of this," said the lady.

"Don't include me in your calculations, Miss Browne," I said. "I don't even know what makes the wheels go round."

"Perhaps not," she replied. "But I do. And did you know that your orderly has been a stoker in vessels running between England and India?"

Strange to say, I did not know it. I was aware that Pathans were to be found on that job; and now I thought of it, although I had never conversed in English with Yakoub Khan, I had on occasions accidentally heard him use expressions which made me wonder what sort of company he had kept at Brighton, where he had gone to recover from wounds received in France. Probably the stokehold, not Brighton, was to blame. I always think, moreover, that it isn't particularly wise to inquire too close into an Afridi's past. Yakoub Khan came, I knew, from the Ut Kheyl, a clan which produces the most expert rifle thieves on the North-West Frontier, and I wouldn't have been the least surprised to hear that he had also served an apprenticeship to that nefarious trade. If he had done so it is little wonder that he was able to move about from the place where we had lain in hiding, up on deck and into the saloon, with impunity.

"And I thought," continued Miss Browne, "that perhaps, as you had been a sailor, you might manage to do some navigating."

This brought me to my senses with a rush. Without stopping to explain I made a dash for the bridge, closely followed by my orderly, who must have thought that the blow I had received had affected my brain. With a shaky hand I opened the lid of the chronometer box in the chart-room. If those had stopped we were in difficulties. In a moment I was reassured.

" When did you say the officers were murdered ? " I asked Miss Browne, who had followed us.

" The night before last," she replied. " Why ? "

" Because these chronometers were wound yesterday morning," I said. From the deck below came the voice of Ah Wong, who had been forward to the forecastle.

" Have got bos'n," he said. I had gathered that the boatswain had been one of the leaders, so not taking any chances, I ordered Yakoub Khan to fetch his rifle, and Ah Wong to wait until it was brought.

" No need him," replied the latter with his usual brevity. " He dead."

We went forward to the forecastle. The boatswain had certainly been, next to Lambro, " the mildest-manner'd man that ever scuttled ship or cut a throat " ; and here he lay with his own scientifically slit from ear to ear. He was lying across a leather trunk, which was unlocked. As the others dragged his body away I opened the trunk, and found amongst other things two charts, which I removed to the chart-room. The following information was extracted from Ah Wong in the evening. We were too busy just then planning our escape to worry over the deceased.

Ah Wong, whom we had promised to forgive if he played the game, had been, like others of the crew, both sailors and firemen, simple seafarers who had been led astray. The supercargo had been the real villain of the piece, and it was his brother who had met the ship at the islands with the junks. I received the impression, however, that there was something even bigger behind these two, and it was perhaps significant that what had raised Yakoub Khan's suspicions was a question, put to him in pure Urdu by one of the saloon stewards, regarding the possibility of his regiment being tampered with.

The boatswain had really been the navigator, although he seemed to have had other ambitions. He was well-educated, and was said to have been at one time an officer in the Chinese Navy. It was he who had wound the chronometers. Differences of opinion had arisen between him and the supercargo just after we left Hong Kong. The boatswain had proposed to alter the ship by painting and other devices, and sell her in a Chinese port, but this the supercargo wisely deemed to be unsafe.

III.

On returning to the bridge I found that one of the charts was of the Anamba Islands in the South China Sea ; the other the Natunas, which lie to the north-east of them. The chart of the Anambas was from a survey made by one of the vessels of our Navy, and was quite modern ; that of the Natunas had been made by the Dutch many years ago, and was not so satisfactory.

The position of the islands, and the fact that the boatswain had the charts in his possession, led me to think that we were anchored in one or the other of the groups. I raked my memory for any information regarding them. The Natunas I was certain I had never heard of, but I remembered that the others had been in the public eye when the ill-fated Russian Baltic fleet was on its way to Tsushima. They belonged to the Dutch, but no white men lived in them.

Luckily my knowledge of sextant and chronometer had been refreshed by some survey work which I had assisted with in China. Finding on the chart on the north-east side of the Great Natuna Island a strait which seemed to resemble the one we were anchored in, I took an observation for longitude with the captain's sextant, the horizon being clear to the south-east, using the latitude of the strait on the chart. It came within two miles of being right, not bad considering that I was rusty and was using strange tools. Now we knew where we were.

It was an ideal place from the pirates' point of view, for I doubt if any vessel would pass there in the course of a year. Right down the east coast of the island such remarks as "unsurveyed" and "coral reefs reported to be extending" were frequent on the chart. It was evidently a sea that was little used. The islands were wooded down to the water's edge, and there was no sign of habitation.

Just after I had found our position, Miss Browne came on the bridge for a consultation. She had found that the fires in one of the boilers had been banked : they had been used for supplying steam to the winches when the cargo was being discharged into the junks, and Yakoub Khan and Ah Wong were stoking up as hard as they could. She thought that we would be able to move in about an hour's time, not very fast, of course, as one boiler was as much as they could manage. That, however, should give us about six knots.

We decided that it would be impossible to keep going night and day : we were too short-handed. We would have to anchor every night, so our best plan was to go through the islands : first the Natunas, then cross over and go down through the Anambas. With any luck after that we might carry on to Singapore. When last seen the junks had been heading for the north end of the Great Natuna Island, and hugging the land with the evident intention of turning off to the westward. We must therefore go down the east side.

It looked a rather difficult undertaking from the chart, but I reckoned that in daylight one could pretty well see the channels. The water over the coral reef was a very light green in appearance ; the rest of the sea varied from a darker green to deep blue, according to the depths. The water was beautifully transparent. We were lying in six fathoms—that is, thirty-six feet—yet we could see the coral bottom quite distinctly. Before going below Miss Browne put the windlass in gear for heaving up the anchor, a job which Ah Wong professed himself able to do.

It was about eleven o'clock in the forenoon when " Stand by " was rung up on the telegraph from the engine-room to indicate that they were ready. I answered it, and told Ah Wong to heave up. He soon reported " Anchor aweigh." I rang up " Full speed ahead," and with a thrill saw the beach on both sides begin to slip past as we slowly headed for the open sea. Once clear of the strait I scanned the horizon to the north for the junks, but they had vanished. I swung the *Chang Chu's* head to the south and hoped for the best.

I watched the coast with my field-glasses as we slowly slid along. For the first thirty miles nothing was to be seen but dense jungle ; then one or two clearings and cocoa-nut plantations came in sight. Here and there I noticed small villages, the huts being made of matting. There was no point in trying to communicate. We had plenty of provisions, coal, and water; we did not know their language, and in any case the natives could be of little use to us. My main idea was to keep off the reefs, and this I managed, but had some narrow shaves. The sea was luckily calm.

Once Miss Browne left the engine-room and came up on the bridge. Ah Wong made tea, and relieved me at the wheel while we drank it. She said that it was pretty hot below, but that Yakoub Khan was working like two men.

Just as the sun was setting I decided to anchor. It would not be safe to go on in the dark, and in any case those below would have had enough of it. We were safe as far as the junks were concerned; indeed I was feeling quite cheery and hopeful. The chart now showed more definite soundings and fewer unsurveyed patches, and once we got across to the Anambas and on to the other chart, the navigation would be comparatively easy.

Soon after we anchored, Ah Wong produced quite a decent meal. I decided that we three men would keep a watch between us, Yakoub Khan and Ah Wong arranging theirs in such a way that between them they could keep the boiler fires going. We were all pretty well dead beat, and it wasn't very long before we turned in.

The next two days were uneventful, as they were spent practically on the open sea. Starting at dawn on the first day I shaped a course for an island that lay between the two groups, where, according to the chart, there was a decent anchorage, and made it in the late afternoon. By the evening of the second day we had reached one of the outer islands of the Anambas, and anchored for the night.

I had really the softest job on board. Most of the time I was at the wheel with the chart on a table beside me. It was, of course, trying to a certain extent, as any one who has spent hours at the wheel of a vessel could imagine, and the monotony was aggravated by the glare of the tropical sun on the calm sea. But at any rate I was in the open air, and it was Paradise compared to the engine-room and stokehold. Occasionally Miss Browne came on to the bridge for a breath of fresh air ; and although she never complained, I could see that she was having a pretty thin time down below. My admiration of the girl's pluck and endurance increased daily.

Ah Wong was the general utility man, and we often agreed that his capture by Yakoub Khan had been a master stroke. He trimmed coal from the bunker into the stokehold, cooked the food, relieved me at the wheel when necessary, hove the lead, and worked the anchor. Like most Chinese of his class, he could not bear to be idle. On one occasion after he had done a hard spell of shovelling coal from the bunker to Yakoub Khan in the stokehold, that worthy had sent him on deck for a rest. During his rest he scrubbed down the poop.

The voyage down through the Anambas, if we had had a full crew, would have been a sheer delight. I had an accurate large-scale chart on which every reef was marked. A light head breeze made the weather ideal. The sea was a deep clear blue, and the islands seemed to be covered with cocoa-nut palms from their rocky summits right down to the white fringe of sand which joined the pale green of the water over the coral reefs. We took two days to get down through the group.

The day on which we stretched from the Anambas across the toe of the South China Sea to the Malay Peninsula, we left before dawn, for we had to make a longer day's run than we had hitherto attempted. Strange to say, we saw no vessels, even after we got into the track of shipping, until after dark, when, having picked up the Horsburgh Light, we were standing in toward the shore to anchor. We then observed the lights of a large steamer bound north. With Ah Wong at the lead I steamed slowly toward the land, and anchored when the water shoaled to five fathoms.

After dinner Miss Browne and I went up on to the poop. It was a glorious moonlight night, dead calm at first. Then came a cooling breeze from the land, which brought with it not unpleasant smells of earth and jungle and the throb and hum of the tropic night. The land breeze had raised a slight sea, and the gently swelling crests of the waves appeared to be polished by the light of the full moon. We leaned against the rail and talked.

What was uppermost in my mind, and doubtless also in that of my companion, was the almost incredible fact that four of us, and one of the four, myself, little better than an amateur, had brought the *Chang Chu* thus far, and that, if all went well, we might complete our task the next day. Yet strange to say, beyond a few remarks about to-morrow's work, we hardly discussed the subject at all. Instead we talked of trout-fishing.

I had mentioned that I hoped to get some in Kashmir, where I intended to spend my leave, and this at once aroused her interest, for apparently, next to engineering, it was her greatest hobby in life. Soon, with real enthusiasm, we were deep in the subject of pools, and runs, of flies, wet and dry, and she interested me greatly with her description of dapping for large trout in a loch near her home in Ireland, a form of sport which I had never seen practised.

Engrossed in the subject although we were, we soon could hardly refrain from yawning. We had had a long day, with the promise of another trying one on the morrow, so she decided to retire. I had a brief look round to see that all was well, and then followed her example.

IV.

The first hitch revealed itself before daylight next morning, when, instead of Ah Wong, Yakoub Khan brought in the breakfast, and explained that the quartermaster had gone. He should have called my orderly at 4 A.M., but the latter himself woke at that time, searched the ship for the quartermaster without result, and at last found a rope's end hanging over the side, down which he must have slid with the idea of swimming ashore. That he bore us no malice was evident, for he had left the steam well up in the boiler, had even cooked our breakfast and laid the table in the saloon. Doubtless he feared an examination by the authorities, and dreaded the result if in the course of it he gave his former companions away.

Apart from other considerations we were both rather sorry, for we had got to like the ex-pirate, who had worked cheerfully and well throughout. If he had got safely ashore he would probably find a countryman keeping a shop in one of the Malay villages along the coast, and be all right. We wished him luck, but in the meantime he had put us in an awkward position, for I could now on no account leave the bridge once we started. I made up my mind to prepare before we got under way for any emergencies that I could foresee. I would put the pilot ladder and boat rope over the side, and hoist the Pilot Jack at the fore.

The most serious predicament in which the desertion of Ah Wong had left us was not discovered until we went on deck. Then in the pale light of the dawn we saw that, having depended entirely on the lead the previous evening, I had gone in much too far, as we were anchored close to the breakers, on to which at the moment a fairly strong tide was setting. The vessel was quite safe provided that she could be got moving ahead as soon as the anchor was broken out of the ground, but the problem was—who was going to heave it up?

Neither Yakoub Khan nor myself knew anything about a steam windlass, and, even if we did, the former was required in the engine-room to help while the engines were being started, while it was obviously useless to start the vessel unless I were at the wheel. Finally, we decided that we should have to take the risk of Miss Browne heaving up and then getting below to start the engines as soon as possible. Afterwards, when the vessel was well under way, she could come up and put the windlass in gear for letting go the anchor, a fairly simple operation which she quickly explained to me.

Everything being ready, I went on the bridge, and Miss Browne commenced to heave in the cable. As the *Chang Chu* was being hove toward her anchor, and for a moment after it was broken out of the ground, she forged slightly ahead, and that was, of course, the time when the engines should have been started had there been any one below to do it. Between then and getting the anchor up clear of the water, it seemed an age; the vessel was gradually drifting closer and closer to the breakers astern. My heart sank. Was bumping helplessly in the breakers to be the ignominious end of our adventure? I could do nothing but watch.

At last I saw Miss Browne shut off the steam from the windlass, give one brief glance at the breakers, and then flee like a startled deer to the engine-room. Almost immediately afterwards the wheeze of steam from below told me that the engines were beginning to move, and just in time we gradually drew clear. Cheerfully I set about the long day's work, and the great red " eye of day " was just peeping over the horizon as I made for the entrance to the Straits.

Shortly after this the light land breeze died away, a dead calm ensued, and the conditions became typical of the Straits of Malacca as most travellers know them. I soon found that owing to refraction I had to watch my bearings very closely, for the clear shimmering atmosphere seemed to enlarge objects, and make them appear much nearer than they were. Two small fishing boats which we passed loomed up like large vessels, and small islands and clumps of trees appeared to be floating well above the water.

About noon the heat became intense, and my sympathies were all with the toilers below. There was a dimness in the air which appeared to be stifling, and the weather looked uncertain and threatening. Presently dense clouds loomed up ahead, which gradually overspread the whole sky, and a thunderstorm, with vivid lightning, broke over the *Chang Chu*, rather unnerving in my loneliness. Having seen it coming I was steering a safe course, and only hoped that I would not meet another vessel, for the rain fell in torrents, so that I could hardly see the forecastle head.

Shortly afterwards it cleared, fell away calm again, and the heat seemed more intense than ever. Then on the southern horizon a darker tint appeared on the blue surface of the water, which remained, then grew larger and approached, and the welcome sea breeze, invigorating and refreshing, was blowing over us, raising sparkling wavelets on the hitherto calm sea. There was a good awning over the bridge, so I had remained dry, and my spirits were rising as we continued to make good progress.

We met several vessels both before and after the squall, and I noticed that we seemed to be rather an object of interest, as several altered course to pass closer. This I expect was due to the fact that we were many days overdue.

About 4 P.M. I could see the buildings of Singapore and the shipping in the harbour. I looked up at the fore-truck: the Pilot Jack was streaming out bravely as we stood toward the port. Presently a smart steam launch made its way toward us. I slowed down, and a sigh of relief escaped me as I saw the pilot climb over the rail. At the same time, I had to laugh outright, probably the first time that I had laughed that day, when I saw his look of blank amazement as he gazed around the empty decks.

" Good gracious, what's the matter here ? " he exclaimed as he came on the bridge, looked for the captain, decided that it must be I, although I was at the wheel, and advanced to shake hands. I explained very briefly the circumstances of the piracy, while the pilot listened attentively. He was a cheery Scotsman, whom it was good to have on board, and as I finished my explanation his hand again shot out and grasped mine in sincere sympathy and congratulation. By this time we were getting among the shipping.

" Well, now, what's to be done about letting go the anchor ? " asked the pilot.

" Oh, I will do that if you can manage up here," I replied confidently. I didn't think it necessary to explain that I had only learned how to do it that morning.

" I can manage here all right. Run along forward now and stand by. I won't risk going too close in amongst the shipping. I will take you ashore in my launch, and the agents can put a crew on board and shift her afterwards."

I went up on the forecastle head, stood by the windlass, and looked toward the bridge. At the pilot's order of " Let go ! " I twisted the brake lever, and the *Chang Chu's* cable rattled out through the hawse-pipe for the last time as far as I was concerned. As I did so I remembered that, while rummaging in the storeroom a few nights before, I had found some champagne. I strolled along toward the bridge, feeling well satisfied with life.

" Have you rung off the engines, pilot ? " I asked.

" I have," he replied.

" Right. As soon as we can collect the chief engineer we will foregather in the saloon and have one big drink. She certainly deserves it."

" *She!* " exclaimed the pilot with startled emphasis.

I nodded my head. " Yes, *she!* " I said.

Printed in Great Britain by
WILLIAM BLACKWOOD & SONS LTD.